Characters of R. John Wright

An Unauthorized Identification & Price Guide

by Shirley Bertrand

Published by Hobby House Press
Grantsville, MD 21536
www.hobbyhouse.com

Photographic Credits:
Beitzel Photography: Front Cover, Back Cover, Illustrations 75, 97, 147, 177
Arthur Kaplan: Illustrations 6, 7, 10, 14, 20, 21, 22, 23, 24, 26, 27, 28, 29, 30, 31, 32, 33, 34, 35, 36, 39, 40, 41, 42, 43, 44, 47, 49, 51, 52, 53, 54, 55, 56, 57, 58, 59, 60, 61, 62, 63, 64, 65, 66, 67, 68, 69, 70, 71, 72, 73, 74, 76, 77, 78, 79, 80, 81, 82, 83, 85, 86, 87, 88, 89, 92, 93, 94, 95, 96, 98, 99, 100, 101, 102, 103, 104, 106, 107, 109, 110, 111, 131, 132, 133, 134, 135, 136, 137, 138, 139, 140, 141, 142, 143, 144, 145, 146, 148, 149
Daniel Kublank: Title Page, Illustrations 1, 2, 3, 4, 9, 11, 12, 13, 15, 16, 17, 18, 19, 25, 37, 38, 45, 46, 48, 108, 112, 113, 114, 115, 116, 117, 118, 119, 120, 121, 122, 123, 124, 125, 127, 128, 130, 150, 151, 158, 159, 160, 162, 163, 169, 172, 173, 174, 175, 176
Photo by Kelly: Illustration 166
Teddy Bear and Friends magazine: Illustrations 129, 170, 178
RJW Collector: 161, 164, 167, 168, 171
R. John Wright Product Catalog: R. John Wright photo on page 6, 90, 91, 156, 157, 165

Front Cover: Left: Christopher Robin and Winnie-the-Pooh Series I. Right: The little Prince Premiere Edition.
Back Cover: Geppetto and Pinocchio II Traditional.
Table of Contents: Jemima Puddle-duck™ and Peter Rabbit™.

Additional copies of this book may be purchased at $29.95 (plus postage and handling) from
Hobby House Press, Inc.
1 Corporate Drive, Grantsville, MD 21536
1-800-554-1447
www.hobbyhouse.com
or from your favorite bookstore or dealer.
©2000 Shirley Bertrand and Hobby House Press, Inc.

Printed in the United States of America

ISBN: 0-87588-592-6

Table of Contents

Illustration 1. Periwinkle.
See page 120.

Illustration 2. Pep.
See page 113.

Illustration 3.
"Flit" Kewpie™
Bug and "Fleur"
Flower Kewpie™.
See page 109.

Illustration 4. Miss Golli
and Golliwog. See page
118.

Acknowledgements

First and foremost, I'd want to thank R. John Wright for creating such brilliant pieces of art. I'd also like to thank those people who put together the R. John Wright sales brochures, the *RJW Collector* (the official Publication for the R. J. Wright Collectors Club), and the R. John Wright Internet who supplied a vast amount of information. Thanks to Shirley Praytor for her article in Teddy Bear and Friends in August 2000, to Deborah Adam Thompson for her Doll Reader article July 1993, and to Krystyna Poray Goddu for her article in Dolls in the May/June 1987 issue. Thanks to Shirley Buchholz for "An Artist in Felt"/The Best of Doll Reader/ Volume 1. And finally, I couldn't have accomplished the writing of this book without the ads from the catalogues of The Enchanted Doll House.

The Mystique of R. John Wright Dolls

When R. John Wright sold his first basket of handmade dolls, I wonder if he had any idea just how far his talents would take him. His determination to learn the trade, as well as his own artistry, has won him the highest praise, not only from doll and bear collectors, but from his fellow artists as well. His first dolls were handcrafted in molds he designed and used in his home on the kitchen table.

The early "old people" were handmade of natural fibers with true dedication to every detail. These dolls are highly sought after by avid R. John Wright collectors and are becoming harder and harder to find. Certain early dolls have been crafted with many variations so that there are very few which are absolutely identical even though they are the same edition.

R. John Wright's next venture was his creation of the Little Children series which included his children — Emily (1984), Arthur (1987 to 1989), Lillian (1987 to 1989) and Patrick (1987 to 1988). He excelled in each and every design. The Little Prince (1983 to 1984), one of the designs in his Little Children series, clearly shows his fantastic talent for detail. This doll is probably one of the most sought after in the series, along with Captain Corey (1982), Max and Pinocchio (1985), and Timothy and Rosemary (1983), all from the Childhood Classics series.

One of R. John Wright's biggest goals was to be affiliated with the Walt Disney Company. He succeeded in this by designing the wonderful 8-inch Winnie-the-Pooh (to go along with Christopher Robin), a very special bear for both bear and R. John Wright collectors alike. Then came Lifesize Pooh in an 18-inch size. Other winning sets were Geppetto and Pinocchio and Snow White and the Seven Dwarfs, both sets of which were based on the Walt Disney Company movies.

As the years have passed, R. John Wright has crafted his dolls with finer and finer detail. I have to say that Peter Rabbit™ (1998 to 1999) is just wonderful. And just when you think he cannot top his last piece, John comes along with yet another winner, such as Jemima Puddle-duck™! What a beautiful piece this is. Then he creates the set of Jemima's Ducklings™ with one unhatched egg. What could possibly top that?

The wooden Garden Wheelbarrow (2000), designed by R. John Wright and produced by artist Michael Langton, is another superb piece for which we can thank John. He has also designed cabbages and vegetables made out of handmade wool felt to fit into the wheelbarrow. What a setting this makes. Beatrix Potter fans are in for a real treat with this piece!

Heidi (2000), with her goat Snowflake, is proof of what I have been saying all along — the way that R. John Wright can translate his ideas into three-dimensional pieces of artwork is truly brilliant.

The Wrights have recently announced that they are working on an 18-inch Pinocchio for Disneyland™. This wooden Pinocchio will be produced by ANRI in Italy from John's design and will be assembled and dressed at the R. John Wright factory. I am sure that the many R. John Wright collectors will eagerly anticipate the arrival of this new production.

When you meet John, you will very likely meet Susan Wright who is right there on his arm. They make a wonderful couple and are very willing to share their knowledge and even their secrets on how some of their characters were conceived and brought into production. Both are artists, but most of all, they are down-to-earth people who have a great sense of humor and are always willing to sign their wonderful creations. What else can we ask for!

R. John Wright Company

Michigan native R. John Wright is truly a superior artist as well as craftsman, as his work will attest. As a student at Wayne State University, John studied literature and art in the liberal arts curriculum. When he left Michigan in 1970, he intended to go to California. Instead, John found himself in New Hampshire.

John's interest in doll making began after reading the book *The Doll* by Carl Fox. In 1972, John met his future wife, Susan who graduated from the University of New Hampshire with a Bachelor of Fine Arts Degree. She not only became John's wife, but also a creative partner who would contribute her talents to doll making as well. John and Susan married in 1974 and made their home in Brattleboro, Vermont.

John found a job in a local hardware store as a clerk and, in 1976, he was very unexpectedly laid off. It was at this time that he was inspired to take advantage of the opportunity and try his hand at creating dolls, something that had been in his mind for some time.

Having never sewn anything before, John's first doll was rather primitive. The doll was very simple — made from pale yellow flannel — and he found that the process came very easily for him. Before finishing his first doll, John had already considered how he could improve upon his first creation.

Shortly after completing his first doll, John created six male dolls out of flesh-

Illustration 1. R. John Wright. *Photo courtesy of R. John Wright Product Catalog.*

colored felt. Their beards and hair were crafted with sheep's wool. Called "Hillbilly Dolls," presumably because of the hillbilly style of their clothing, these first dolls were taken to a craft gallery. Retailing for $28 each, the dolls sold quickly. Jean Schramm, then owner of The Enchanted Doll House, was one of the first to carry R. John Wright dolls.

Over the next six months, John continued to make these primitive felt dolls and marketed them to area craft stores. Susan, a talented artist herself, proved an able collaborator with her husband, and together, they researched every aspect of doll making. They were able to improve upon the dolls and provide them with joints as well as more sophisticated clothing. Research included taking a Lenci doll to the hospital and having it X-rayed. John readily admits to being inspired by Steiff as well as Lenci and Kathe Kruse dolls, having played with Steiff dolls and toys as a child.

The demand for the dolls soon outgrew the small ground-floor apartment that had substituted as a doll factory. Juried craft shows held throughout New England proved to be an excellent source of orders from both wholesalers and retailers. This expanding market led John and Susan to a cottage-type industry as they hired more and more people to help them with their work.

Within a year of creating that first doll, John tried his hand at sculpting faces and these developed into his first molded felt dolls. He designed males and females, attired in costumes reminiscent of their homelands and appropriately accessorized. Because these dolls were handmade in a cottage industry setting, there were variations of clothing, colors, fabrics and shoes. When there was a shortage of a fabric or accessory item, something similar would be used instead. Some of the socks were cotton but the majority of the old ones were hand-knit by Susan Wright who was, and is, responsible for knitting the scarves as well as all the wool socks. The shoes were all handmade using their own patterns to insure that they were all original. John's attention to detail on his dolls is one of the factors that make his dolls so highly collectible. His dolls seem to have a personality all their own.

The Little Children Series debuted in 1980, coinciding with the birth of John and Susan's first child. These dolls were an instant hit with collectors and the demand for these charming dolls soared.

The Wrights decided to relocate the business to Cambridge, New York. The production of the dolls increased due to the new equipment that had been developed especially for doll making. This increase in production enabled John to exhibit his dolls at the 1985 International Toy Fair held in New York City. It was at this event that John showed his first prototype of Christopher Robin and Winnie-the-Pooh, which was produced under license from the Walt Disney Company. Other animal characters and dolls were produced under the Walt Disney Company license in the succeeding years.

Accessories have always been very important to the total concept of R. John Wright creations. Many of the older dolls had rakes, sticks, brooms or crooks. These were all hand-carved by Quaker craftsmen who also made large size versions of these tools. The baskets that some of the dolls carry were custom made for John by a basket-making family in North Carolina that John had met while doing craft fairs early in his doll-making career.

Some of the wooden items that accompany his dolls have been produced by other artists, but always under the guidance of R. John Wright himself, who furnishes the sample or pattern and designs. ANRI made the Pinocchio in 1992 and the Geppetto's Chair at about the same time. Another superior wood craftsman, Michael Langton, has also carried out wood projects for R. John Wright from time to time.

Packaging of the dolls is also an important feature. Most of the old people did not come in boxes. The early children were first shipped in white cardboard boxes. The early white boxes did not hold up well and often did not last. However, true to form, the Wrights sought out a terrific box manufacturer. The boxes are beautifully made and they do enhance the doll even more as well as hold up very well.

In September of 1979, R. John Wright was elected to the National Institute of American Doll Artists (NIADA), a prestigious doll artist association. Many of his early dolls carry the small silver NIADA stickers on the hangtags.

There are two variations of hangtags on the early dolls. One is an oval tag with silhouettes of two people facing each other doffing their hats. All it says is "Made by R. John Wright, Brattleboro, Vermont." The next tag is a fold-over tag with "R. John Wright" dolls and images of Mario, MacTavish and Elsa on the front. Inside it reads "This doll is handmade of felt using an adaptation of a steam-mold process which was popular in the 1920's. This technique produces detailed facial contours by hot-pressing a starched sheet of felt in a series of operations using original molds. The completed head is then jointed to an all felt body with movable limbs and stuffed with kapok and cotton. The features of the face are hand painted and the hair, which is of natural fibers, is sewn directly to the scalp. All clothing, including the hats and shoes, is cut and sewn from original patterns. There is an identifying signature silk screened on the bottom of the left foot." These early people are 18 inches tall.

Timeline of R. John Wright Dolls

1976   First Doll
        Hillbilly Dolls

1977 to 1978   L1 (Bearded Old Man
                 With Stick)
               F1 (Giuseppi)
               A1 (Mario)
               J1
               P1 (Luigi)
               S1 (Father Christmas)
               G2
               B2 (Old Lady With Rake)
               H2 (Maria)
               K2 (Christina)
               M1 (Rosa)

1978 to 1979   Elfs and Imps

1979 to 1980   Periwinkle

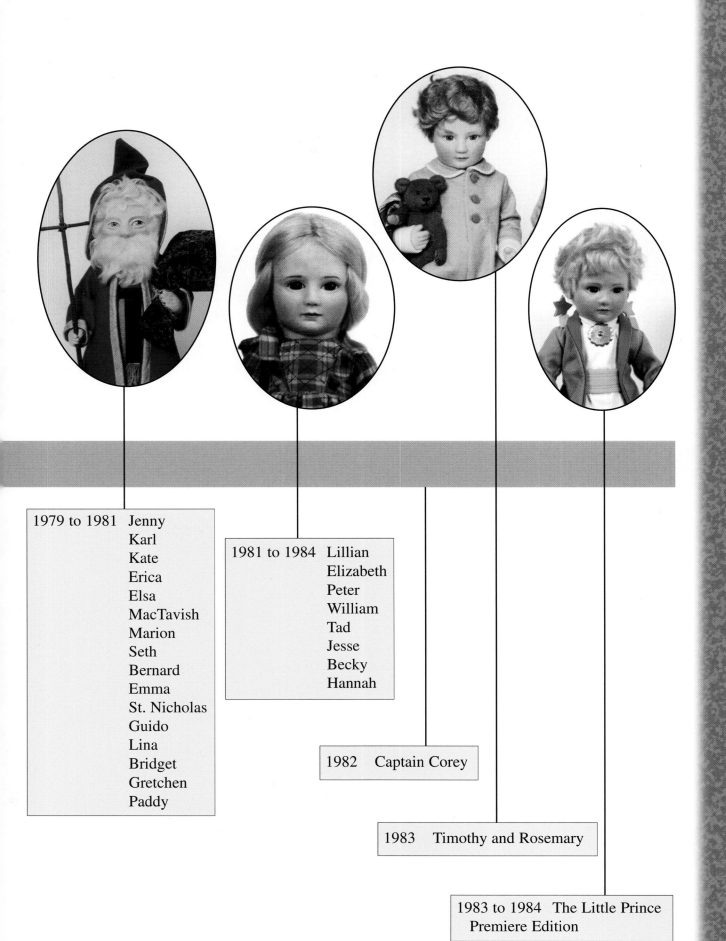

1979 to 1981   Jenny
Karl
Kate
Erica
Elsa
MacTavish
Marion
Seth
Bernard
Emma
St. Nicholas
Guido
Lina
Bridget
Gretchen
Paddy

1981 to 1984   Lillian
Elizabeth
Peter
William
Tad
Jesse
Becky
Hannah

1982   Captain Corey

1983   Timothy and Rosemary

1983 to 1984   The Little Prince
Premiere Edition

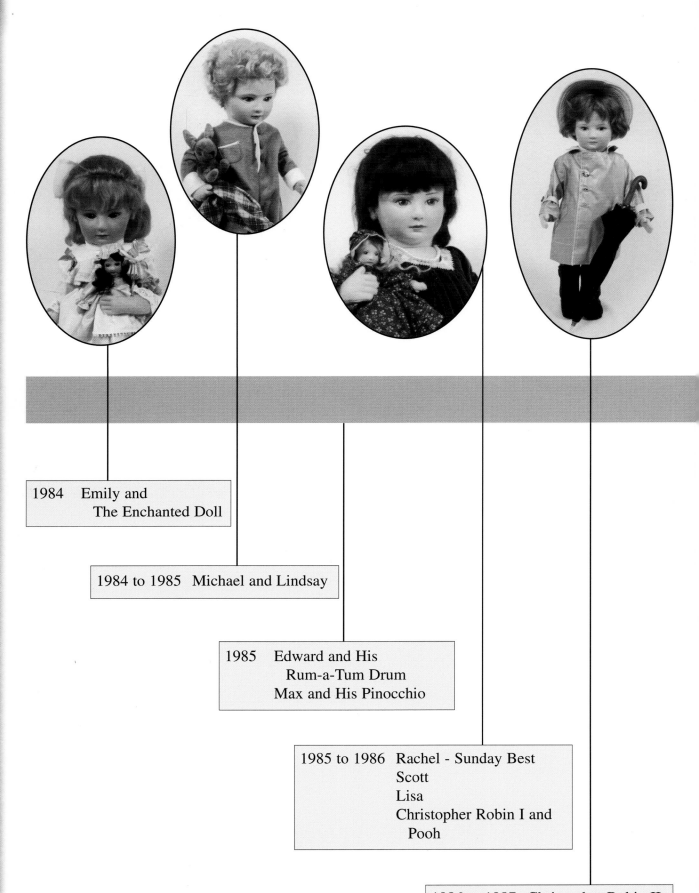

1984   Emily and
          The Enchanted Doll

1984 to 1985   Michael and Lindsay

1985   Edward and His
          Rum-a-Tum Drum
Max and His Pinocchio

1985 to 1986   Rachel - Sunday Best
Scott
Lisa
Christopher Robin I and
          Pooh

1986 to 1987   Christopher Robin II
Piglet
Eeyore

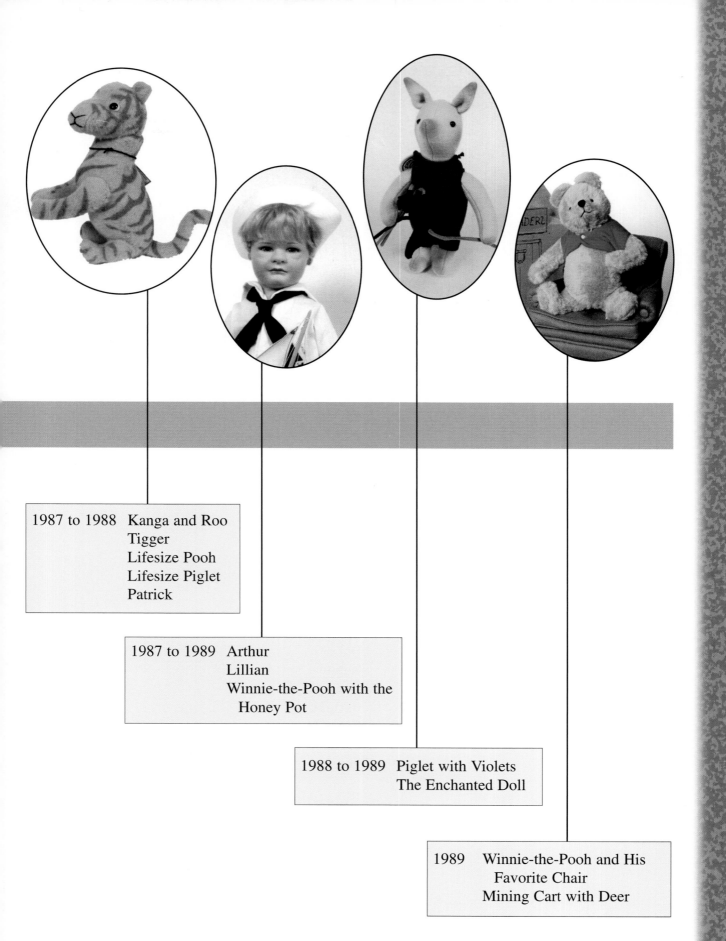

1987 to 1988   Kanga and Roo
                Tigger
                Lifesize Pooh
                Lifesize Piglet
                Patrick

1987 to 1989   Arthur
                Lillian
                Winnie-the-Pooh with the
                    Honey Pot

1988 to 1989   Piglet with Violets
                The Enchanted Doll

1989   Winnie-the-Pooh and His
                    Favorite Chair
                Mining Cart with Deer

1988 to 1991   Little Red Riding Hood

1989 to 1993   Snow White in Rags

1989 to 1994   Snow White - Princess
               Dopey
               Happy
               Doc
               Bashful
               Grumpy
               Sleepy
               Sneezy

1990 to 1992   Hans and Gretel Brinker

1992   Frightened Dopey
          Mary, Mary, Quite Contrary
          Pinocchio
          Geppetto's Chair
          Pleasure Island Pinocchio

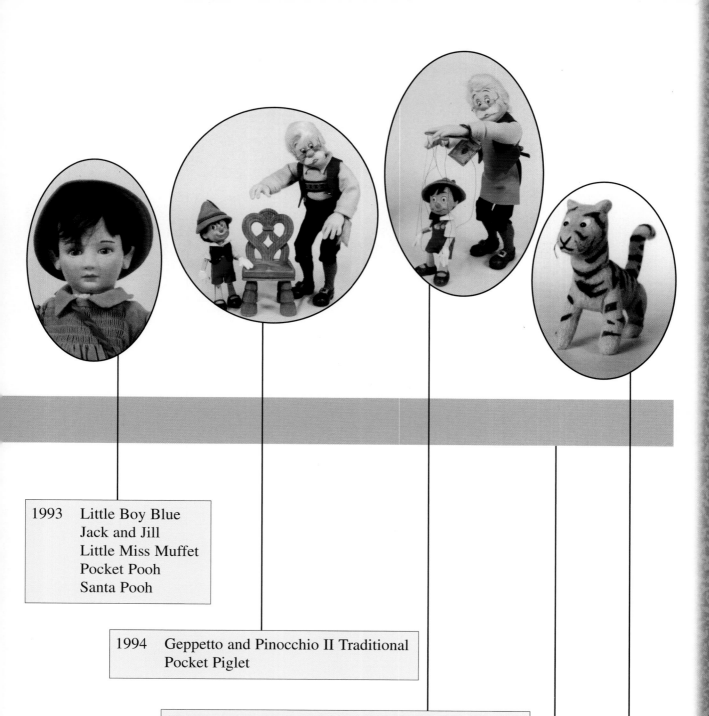

1993   Little Boy Blue
        Jack and Jill
        Little Miss Muffet
        Pocket Pooh
        Santa Pooh

1994   Geppetto and Pinocchio II Traditional
        Pocket Piglet

1994 to 1995   Geppetto and Pinocchio I Marionette

1995   Pocket Eeyore
        Wintertime Pooh and Piglet

1996   Geppetto Searches for
            Pinocchio
        Pocket Tigger
        Wintertime Eeyore

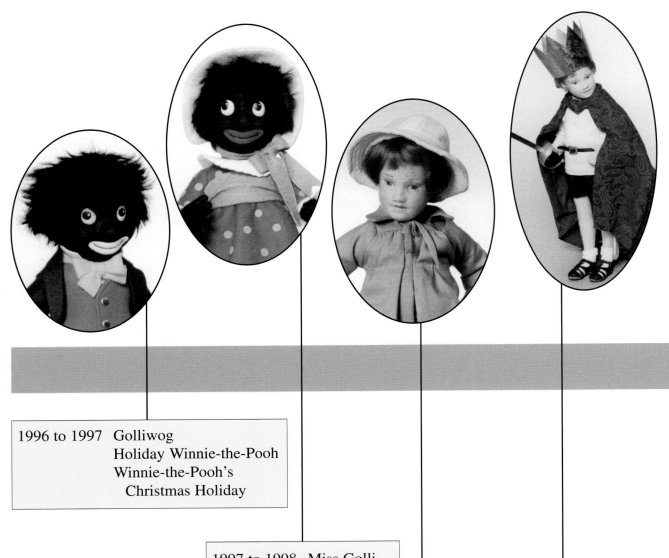

1996 to 1997　Golliwog
　　　　　　　Holiday Winnie-the-Pooh
　　　　　　Winnie-the-Pooh's
　　　　　　　Christmas Holiday

1997 to 1998　Miss Golli
　　　　　　　Teddy Bear

1997 to 1999　Christopher Robin (12-inch)
　　　　　　　Christopher Robin (12-inch) and Pooh

1998　　King Christopher Robin
　　　　This Calls For A Celebration!
　　　　Pocket Rabbit

1999　Silly Old Bear
　　　Periwinkle Pincushion
　　　Pocket Kanga and Roo
　　　Partytime Tigger and Eeyore
　　　PoohBee
　　　Bear's Bed
　　　Pocket Owl
　　　United Federation of Doll Club
　　　　Boutonniere Kewpie®
　　　"Fleur" Flower Kewpie®
　　　Christopher Robin and Pooh
　　　　Bedtime
　　　Wintertime Christopher Robin
　　　"Flit" Kewpie® Bug
　　　Vespers

2000　Bao-Bao
　　　Jemima Puddle-duck™
　　　Klassic Kewpie® (8-inch)
　　　Boutonniere Kewpie®
　　　Heidi
　　　Pinocchio — Walt Disney
　　　　Company Editionn
　　　Jemima's Ducklings™
　　　Kewpie® and Teddy
　　　Hottentot Kewpie®
　　　Garden Wheelbarrow

2000 to 2001　Benjamin Bunny™
　　　　　　Paddington™ Bear
　　　　　　Millennium Kewpie®
　　　　　　The Little Prince
　　　　　　　Centary Edition
　　　　　　Curious George
　　　　　　Tickles
　　　　　　Nippy
　　　　　　Pep
　　　　　　Joey
　　　　　　GolliBabies
　　　　　　RJW Bear Boutonniere

Early Character Dolls

R. John Wright's very early dolls, dating from 1976 to 1977, have a center seam down the front of the face with the mouth sewn in place, a floppy body construction and round exterior joints almost like large white buttons. The heads were formed by sewing and stuffing. Each face is flat with the facial features painted on in black ink. Their large noses are cut into the pattern, since they are not molded like the later ones. Light brown wool felt was used for these earlier dolls. These dolls are approximately 18 inches tall and have large mitt hands resembling a baseball glove with stitches to define the fingers. Most of R. John Wright's early dolls were male and they all had beards and hair of natural fibers, including Alpaca, New Zealand wool and yak hair.

The "First Doll" by R. John Wright is a one-of-a-kind, made on November 11, 1976, of yellow flannel with sheep's wool stuffing and has exterior joints and button eyes. Owned by R. John Wright, the doll is in his personal archives.

The next dolls produced were also primitive looking and are known to collectors today as Hillbilly Dolls because of their country style clothing. Made between 1976 and 1977, there were a total of about 55 Hillbilly Dolls produced and less than half were women.

Early Old Woman

The early Old Woman (1976), shown in Illustration 6, is, in the artist's words, "a rare collector's item." Referred to as the Old Woman by the artist, she has hand-painted features and is a good example of his first work. Her clothing is very plain — she wears an orange bolero jacket over her print top with matching orange shoes and a gathered brown skirt. Her mohair wig has a center part and braids coiled over each ear. She is signed on the bottom of the right foot "WRIGHT."

Illustration 6. Early Old Woman, one of the Hillbilly Dolls.

Early Old Man

A companion piece to the Old Woman seen in Illustration 6, is the early Old Man (1976), shown in Illustration 7, as he is referred to by the artist. He also has features painted on a flat surface. He is wearing tweed pants, a blue shirt and a brown wool vest. His gray hair, which is fringed around his ears, is matted and he has a balding appearance with long sideburns. His ears are rather large with the seam running through the edge of the ear. He is not signed. This example is barefoot but some have slip-on shoes and others wear clothing in a variety of colors. Both the Old Woman and the Old Man have the very large mitt style hands.

Illustration 7. Early Old Man, one of the Hillbilly Dolls.

Character Dolls

For his later dolls, John developed a process whereby a flat sheet of felt is steam molded over an original form which is first sculpted in clay, thereby forming facial contours. The features are then hand-painted while the wigs are made of all natural fibers — Alpaca, karakul, or New Zealand wool and yak hair. Each doll is approximately inches tall with rotating joints at the shoulders and hips that allow them to assume many standing or sitting positions. All the clothing is from original patterns and is completely removable, having snaps, buttonholes and buttons of various materials. The accessories include many wood and leather items.

While the Wrights said that they did not always name the old people or old characters, they did give them numbers or letters. However, many shop owners who sold the dolls did name them, sometimes writing the name on the back of the oval tag. In some instances, the dolls came with a registration card, complete with the name.

Much of the information about the names and dates of the dolls is derived from ads placed by shops that carried the R. John Wright dolls. The 1978 to 1979 Enchanted Doll House catalog pictured Giuseppi, 2JF1; Maria, 2JH2; Rosa, 2JM1; Christina, 2JK2; Mario, 2JA1; and Luigi, 2JP1, at prices ranging from $60 to $70. Six dolls are shown in the catalog for 1979 to 1980: Seth, with a pitchfork (2JS1); Guido, with a black mustache (2JG1); Emma, with a broom (2JE1); Elsa, with a brimmed hat (2JE2); MacTavish, with a tam although he also came in a helmet-type hat (2JM1); and Jenny, in a babushka (2JJ2). The 1980 to 1981 catalog lists Paddy, with the pipe, 2JP1; Kate, with a basket, 2JK2; Gretchen, with a crook, 2JG2; and Karl, with a staff, 2JK1.

Illustration 8. R. John Wright's first brochure featuring drawings of the dolls available identified by letter and number.

R. John Wright Brochure

R. JOHN WRIGHT • DOLLS

These dolls are made entirely of wool felt by R. John Wright of Brattleboro, Vermont. The facial contours are the result of a process whereby a flat sheet of felt is steam molded over an original form which is first sculpted in clay. The features are then hand painted. Wigs are made of all natural fibers, among them: alpaca, karakul, New Zealand wool and yak hair. The height of the dolls is approximately 17 inches. With rotating joints at shoulders and hips they can assume many standing or sitting positions. The clothing is all from original patterns and is completely removable having snaps, buttonholes and real pearl buttons. The accessories include many wood and leather items. Each doll has an identifying signature silkscreened on the bottom of the left foot.

Old Lady with Stick

B2 (1977 to 1978), seen in Illustration 9, is depicted as an Old Lady With Rake. Her dark brown mohair is pulled back and pinned to the back of her head, which is covered with a scarf tied at the back of the neck. Her eyes are so dark brown they look almost black. She is barefoot, wears a red and white cotton dress with a paisley print overskirt, and has her original tag on her wrist. The rake is made of oak.

Illustration 9. B2, Old Lady With Rake.

Old Man with Stick

The Bearded Old Man With Stick (1977 to 1978), seen in Illustration 10, is very similar to MacTavish (see Illustration 42). He wears the same pants and carries the same stick as MacTavish. His costume includes a tan vest, a plaid cotton shirt with a brown scarf, a blue tam and soft-soled slip-on shoes. He is shown in early ads as L1.

Illustration 10. Bearded Old Man With Stick.

Christina

Christina (1977 to 1978), seen in Illustration 11, is the companion to Luigi (see Illustration 12) and is shown in early ads with him as K2. She also has bright red hair and is wearing a print dress with a brown felt vest.

Illustration 11. Christina, shown in early ads as a companion to Luigi.

Luigi

Luigi (1977 to 1978), seen in Illustration 12, has very bright red hair and beard and carries a large rake. He is dressed in a green felt jacket with a leather belt, checked wool pants, a wine-colored cap and is barefoot with leather leggings. He is shown in early ads as P1.

Illustration 12. Luigi with red hair and beard.

Father Christmas

Father Christmas (1977 to 1978), seen in Illustration 13, listed in an ad as S1, has a wonderful white beard and wig. He has the dark complexion of the earlier dolls as well as the large hands. Each of his dark eyes has a white highlight, giving him a piercing look. He wears a white-on-white gown with sleeves and a white hood under a sleeveless robe of wine-colored wool trimmed in black and white checked braid. He is bound at the waist with a wine-colored tie. Father Christmas carries a cross made of two sticks lashed together with a leather thong. Sometimes he has a wicker basket for his gifts.

Illustration 13. Father Christmas with his flowing white beard.

G2

G2 (1977 to 1978), seen in Illustration 14, has no name. The only reference made to this doll is a flier put out by the company referring to her as style G2. She has sandy blonde hair in braids coiled over her ears under a large brimmed felt hat. She can also be found wearing a blue felt hat as well as a tan hat. Wearing a cotton print blouse, a gathered skirt, a tan bolero-style jacket and carrying a crook, she bears a strong resemblance to Jenny, seen in Illustration 35.

Illustration 14. Unnamed G2.

Giuseppi

Giuseppi (1977 to 1978), seen in Illustrations 15, 16 and 17, is shown in some of the early ads as F1. He has a receding hairline, steel-gray beard and hair, and eyes with a piercing look to them. His clothing, which comes in many variations, is simple and reminiscent of an Amish farmer. He wears cotton pants with suspenders and a long-sleeved cotton shirt. His boots are handmade and lace up the front. One version has a handmade straw hat. A second has a black felt hat while a third has a brown one. Each carries a handmade three-pronged oak pitchfork.

Illustration 15. Giuseppi with a straw hat and pitchfork.

Illustration 16. Giuseppi with a lighter gray beard, a black hat, and pitchfork.

Illustration 17. Giuseppi with a brown hat and pitchfork.

Maria

Illustration 18. Maria with a brown laced cummerbund and shoes.

Maria (1977 to 1978), seen in Illustrations 18 and 19, has a dark complexion and long dark hair pulled back into one long braid. Each of her dark eyes has a dot in them which, combined with her smiling mouth, give her a wonderful expression. Maria has many outfits but generally, it is only the print of her skirt and the color of her laced cum- merbund and shoes that differ. Her print skirt is topped with a plain blouse. One example wears a brown felt laced cummer- bund and has brown felt shoes with one strap over the foot while the other example has a pink felt laced cummerbund and pink felt shoes. She also comes wearing a variety of scarves and hats.

24

Illustration 19. Maria wearing a pink laced
cummerbund and shoes.

Illustration 20.
Mario with
brown shoes.

Mario (1977 to 1978), seen in Illustrations 20 and 21, appears in the early ads as A1. He has a dark complexion with a black mohair wig and a bushy black mustache. He wears a wine-colored felt cap, a button-down wine felt vest with pockets over a cotton shirt and pants that can be found in gray wool or cotton. Both are wearing soft-soled shoes — one pair is brown and the other is black. Mario bears a strong resemblance to Guido, seen in Illustrations 22, 23 and 24, and the two are often mistaken for one another.

Illustration 21. Mario wearing plaid pants
and black shoes.

Guido

Guido (1979 to 1981), seen in Illustrations 22, 23 and 24, is shown here out of chronological order so that he may be compared with Mario. Guido is very distinctive with his black curly hair and mustache. He wears a vest, pants and shirt with a thin shoestring-type tie at his neck. His brown leather shoes are an oxford style. Variations of Guido can be found with several color combinations. One example might have a darker complexion with straighter hair and wear a fine brown checked shirt and a dark brown vest with gold buttons and rust-colored or brown corduroy pants, while another, with a light complexion, wears a brown striped shirt and pants with a tiny brown check.

While Mario and Guido are very much alike in appearance, there are some subtle differences. Both have black mohair wigs and bushy mustaches. Mario is usually made of the dark flesh-tone felt while Guido can be found in both shades of flesh-colored felt. Although their clothing is very similar, the trousers come in a variety of materials such as wool, cotton or corduroy. However, unlike Guido, Mario's trousers are usually a print. Both wear a flat hat with a bill, usually in brown or a wine color. Their shoes can be handmade leather or wool felt. Mario has a pullover vest with two silver buttons at the neck while Guido wears an open vest with two or three buttons.

Illustration 22. Guido wearing a three-button vest and checked pants.

Illustration 23. Guido wearing a two-button vest and light colored pants.

Illustration 24. Guido wearing wine-colored corduroy pants.

28

Illustration 25. Two Rosas, the one carrying the basket has "Rosa" hand-written on
her hangtag.

Rosa (1977 to 1978), seen in Illustration 25, is listed in the early ads as M1. The doll on the left is an older lady with gray hair up in a knot. She has a dark complexion, a huge smiling mouth with brown painted side-glancing eyes. She wears a green print blouse, a dark blue cotton skirt under a brown and white checked apron and a scarf of white dotted swiss crisscrossing at her neck. She has "Rosa" handwritten on the back of her hangtag. Her hair is more of a plain bun while the doll above has her hair braided in a bun. Although they are both dressed similarly and both wear shawls and aprons over their dresses, they do not look much alike. The one on the left carries a basket and the one on seen above has a rolling pin in her pocket. Rosa also comes with a knitted shawl and in a completely different outfit.

Bernard (1979 to 1981), seen in Illustrations 26, 27 and 28, is a classy young gentleman with brown hair parted to the side, brown eyes and a light complexion. He has a homemade wicker basket on his back held on by straps made of brown wool felt. His shirt hangs loosely over his orange felt knickers. His cotton socks are knee-high and his shoes are leather-topped slip-ons with wooden bottoms. He can be found in different colored shirts and neck scarves.

Illustration 26. Bernard with his basket, in a gray cotton shirt with a plaid scarf.

Illustration 27. Bernard and his basket, wearing a plaid shirt with a solid scarf.

Illustration 28. Back view of the two Bernards seen in Illustrations 26 and 27.

Bridget (1979 to 1981), not shown, has not been located. She is described in one of the ads as a brunette wearing a dress of cotton tattersall with underskirt and felt sabots. She has a handcrafted straw hat and an oak cane. It appears from the ad that her apron is plaid or checkered.

Erica

Erica (1979 to 1981), seen in Illustrations 29 and 31, has black hair pulled to the back where fine braids form a bun over each ear. On her head, she has a dark brimmed hat with flowers on it. She wears a green felt skirt with a white dotted swiss blouse, a cotton print apron and a laced cummerbund. Her shawl is light blue cotton and she wears a brimmed steel-gray hat adorned with a few felt flowers. Her limited edition tag on the dress says "EZ-17."

Illustration 29. Erica in her brimmed steel-gray hat.

Elsa

Elsa (1979 to 1981), seen in Illustrations 30 and 31, is almost identical to Erica (see Illustrations 29 and 31) except she has a light tan hat made of felt. Elsa's complexion is also darker than Erica's and the Elsa shown here is one inch shorter than Erica is. Notice now similar the dresses are to one another.

Illustration 30. Elsa, almost identical to Erica except for her tan hat.

Illustration 31. A group shot with two Elsas (in tan hats) and Erica in the steel-gray hat, showing how closely they resemble one another.

Emma

Emma (1979 to 1981), seen in Illustrations 32 and 33, has a brown mohair wig with traces of gray running through it. Both examples shown here are wearing gold felt dresses with cotton neck scarves. One has a calico apron while the other has an eyelet apron. Emma can be found in many variations and with many different accessories. Usually she wears an olive green wool felt dress. She may have a hat or a wool scarf and an eyelet apron or a print one. Her hair is usually steel gray with flecks of gray. She may carry a broom, a basket, a rake or a crook.

Illustration 32. Emma with an eyelet apron and carrying a crook.

Illustration 33. Emma with a calico apron and a broom.

34

Gretchen

Illustration 34. Gretchen with her flower-adorned crook.

Gretchen (1979 to 1981), seen in Illustration 34, has soft strawberry blonde hair parted in the middle with braids on either side. She wears a green felt skirt with a band of gray felt trim, a tan cotton apron and a brown fitted vest over a white cotton blouse with black dots. She has a pale blue cotton scarf around her neck and a black felt hat on her head. Her slip-on black felt shoes have pompons on them. The crook she carries is adorned with felt flowers.

Jenny

Jenny (1979 to 1981), seen in Illustration 35, can be found in many variations, but usually wears an olive green wool felt bolero, a cotton plaid skirt and a babushka on her head. She is usually a blonde with a hat or a scarf on her head and carries a stick or sometimes a crook.

Illustration 35. Jenny in her babushka.

Karl (1979 to 1981), seen in Illustration 36, is a young man with a big dark bushy mustache, dark hair and blue eyes. His heavy green felt lederhosen-type shorts have silver buttons holding up the front flap. He wears a sleeveless tan shirt under a wine jacket with cuffs, a green felt Alpine hat, brown tweed knit socks and brown leather shoes with leather ties. He carries a gnarled apple wood walking stick.

Illustration 36. Karl with his gnarled walking stick.

Kate (1979 to 1981) is shown in the ads in the 1980 to 1981 catalogs from The Enchanted Doll House as 2JK2. She is shown wearing a shawl and carrying a basket. Her dress is all felt and covered with a half apron. Somewhere along the line, the name "Kate" was used again, this time in reference to K2 Kate, seen in Illustrations 37 and 39, with a darker complexion and big brown eyes. Her deep red hair is pulled to the back and tiny braids form a bow on the back of her head. Felt flowers are sewn into the right side of the hair. Her skirt is green felt with a one-inch ruffle at the bottom. The blouse is off-white with little green clovers topped off by a front-buttoned gold vest. She wears brown cotton socks and black felt shoes with leather ties. This doll has a typed NIADA card signed by R. John Wright himself, dated "12-15-79."

Illustration 37. Close-up showing the detail of the flowers sewn in her hair.

NIADA

This is to certify that this doll ___.#K2 Kate_____

Red hair w/felt flowers,blouse,skirt & vest

was made by me and sold on ___September 5, 1979_____

to _____

address_____

and is registered with the **NATIONAL INSTITUTE OF AMERICAN DOLL ARTISTS INC.**

R. John Wright

___12-15-79___   R. John Wright
Date

This doll design is the property of the artist & may not be reproduced.

Illustration 38. The identification card accompanying Kate.

Illustration 39. Kate, so identified by a typed NIADA card signed and dated by R. John Wright.

Lina

Lina (1979 to 1981), seen in Illustrations 40 and 41, has a dark brown mohair wig covered by a print scarf. She wears a muslin blouse, a wool felt skirt, and bright colored painted wooden beads around her neck. Her shoes are made of brown leather. There is an edition tag stapled to the back of her skirt that says "L2-27." Lina carries a homemade woven basket that is either filled with felt zucchini, tomatoes and eggplant or is empty.

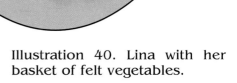

Illustration 40. Lina with her basket of felt vegetables.

Illustration 41. Lina carrying an empty basket.

MacTavish

MacTavish (1979 to 1981), seen in Illustration 42, with a blonde wig and beard, brown eyes and a nice smile. He is wearing a tam, which can be either green or brown and has a tassel on the back. He wears brown corduroy pants with a white felt shirt with pockets and a button in the center. His wool scarf is brown tweed and he has brown soft-soled shoes with ties.

In the early ads with the drawings, L1 was called the Bearded Old Man With Stick (see Illustration 10) and later reappeared as MacTavish. Note the similarity to the doll shown as L1 in shoes, pants and smile. However, MacTavish's hat is much fuller, his hair is bushy and his vest is a different style. Both wear long wool scarves and carry sticks. The earlier doll, L1, has a darker complexion and a balding hairline that goes way back on his head, while MacTavish has a full head of hair. One example has more of a helmet-style hat that is dark blue and he wears dark blue pants as well. MacTavish's walking stick is made out of apple wood, harvested by an acquaintance of John's.

Illustration 42. MacTavish.

Marion

Marion (1979 to 1981), seen in Illustration 43, has brown hair and brown eyes. Her edition tags says "MZ-16." She wears a navy blue wool felt jacket with burgundy trim over a white blouse and a plaid cotton skirt of bright red, blue, green and white. Marion has a knit scarf around her neck and a burgundy tam with a tassel pulled down to one side over her hair. Her shoes are made of brown leather.

Illustration 43. Marion in her tasseled tam.

Paddy

Paddy (1979 to 1981), seen in Illustration 44, comes with a handmade clay pipe. An Irish-looking fellow, wearing a long green felt vest with two baggy covered pockets and buttons down the front over a tan shirt, he has red hair with long sideburns. He wears wine-colored short pants, orange cotton socks and brown leather shoes laced up the front with leather shoestrings. His plaid scarf is cotton and tied loosely around his neck. On his head, he wears a handmade brown wool felt hat. There is a loop from the forefinger to the thumb to rest his pipe in so it will not fall. Two kinds of pipes were made for Paddy. He is shown in only one ad in The Enchanted Doll House catalog for 1980 to 1981.

Illustration 44. Paddy with his clay pipe.

St. Nicholas

St. Nicholas (1979 to 1981), seen in Illustrations 45 and 46, was made a short time after Father Christmas (see Illustration 7) and is a limited edition of 250. He has a lovely soft white beard and hair. He carries a drawstring bag or a basket. The cross he carries is made of two sticks lashed together with a leather thong. St. Nicholas was sold in boxes while Father Christmas was not.

Illustration 45. St. Nicholas in his scarlet hooded cloak trimmed with a white band and carrying a drawstring bag which varies from a gray or wine multi-colored print in a velour fabric.

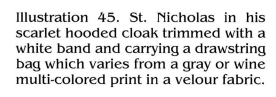

Illustration 46. St. Nicholas in a scarlet cloak with gold colored trim and carrying a basket.

Seth

Seth (1979 to 1981), shown in Illustrations 47 and 48, is very similar to Giuseppi (see Illustrations 15, 16 and 17), even carrying a pitchfork, but his brown mohair is fuller and darker and topped off with a large brimmed brown hat. He wears blue pants with suspenders that fasten to the leather loops on his pants and a red plaid cotton shirt. His handmade leather boots lace up the front. Other examples wear dark pants, black hats and a variety of plaid shirts. One version carries a three-pronged pitchfork while another carries a four-pronged pitchfork.

Illustration 47. Seth with his three-pronged pitchfork.

Illustration 48. Seth carrying a four-pronged pitchfork.

The Old Lady with the Chicken, not shown, is almost impossible to find as only two or three were ever produced and they were marketed near where the Wrights live.

J1, not shown, is listed in one of the early ads but a doll resembling the drawing seen in the ad has not been located to date. He is similar to Bernard, seen in Illustrations 26, 27 and 28, without the basket.

Elves and Imps

Periwinkle (1978 to 1979) is the trademarked logo for the R. John Wright company. Only 7 inches tall, Periwinkle has a loop on his back for hanging and is fully jointed with an olive green wool felt body, arms and legs. His hands, face and pointed ears are of flesh-toned wool felt and he wears a helmet-style pointed hat in dark olive green. The face appears to be hand-painted with the traditional white dot in the pupil of each eye. Three little silver buttons adorn his front, along with a large white collar around his neck. Two pair of blue organdy wings with black stitching are attached to his upper back right about where the hanging loop is attached.

Periwinkle

Illustration 49. Three versions of Periwinkle, the trademarked logo for the R. John Wright company. The one on the left and the one on the right have molded faces and still have their tags. The one in the center is one of only two prototypes made, with a soft face and the center seam down the front.

$\mathcal{L}$ ittle Children

In 1980, the Little Children series was premiered. According to a brochure describing them, they are original dolls made of felt with molded faces and hand-painted features. The finest quality of imported mohair was used in their wigs. They stand 17 inches tall and are fully jointed for flexibility. All of their clothing and accessories are handmade from original designs and are completely removable. These limited edition dolls are signed, dated and numbered and could be registered in the owner's name with the National Institute of American Doll Artists (NIADA), the organization to which R. John Wright belongs.

Original Felt Dolls

R. John Wright

The Little Children™ are original dolls made of felt with molded faces and hand painted features. Wigged using the finest quality imported mohair, they stand 17" tall and are fully jointed for moveability. All clothing and accessories are handmade from original designs and are completely removable. These limited edition dolls are signed, dated, and numbered and may be registered in the owner's name with the National Institute of American Doll Artists.

Little Children™
SERIES I

R. John Wright Dolls
118 West Main Street, Cambridge, New York 12816

Little Children™

HANNAH
JESSE
LILLIAN
PETER

WILLIAM
ELIZABETH
TAD
BECKY

Illustration 50. Brochure showing the Little Children Series I.

Hannah

Hannah (1981 to 1984), seen in Illustrations 51, 52 and 53, from the Little Children Series I, is a limited edition of 250. She has soft brown eyes and a soft blonde mohair wig parted in the center. The plaid of her dress varies as does her hair style and thickness of the hair. She wears long white socks and brown tie shoes.

Illustration 51. Hannah in a dress of wine, pink and peach plaid.

Illustration 52. Hannah in a dress of green and red plaid.

Illustration 53. Hannah in a dress of blue and yellow plaid.

Illustration 54. Two examples of Becky.

Becky (1981 to 1984), seen in Illustration 54, from the Little Children Series I, is a limited edition of 250. She has brown eyes and her auburn hair is pulled back and braided into two thin braids. She wears a brown cotton dress with print sleeves and collar, a natural straw hat, red shoes and carries a rake. The prints used and the size of the straw hat vary as does the facial coloring.

Peter

Peter (1981 to 1984), seen in Illustrations 55 and 56, from the Little Children Series I, is a limited edition of 250 dolls. He has blonde curly hair and blue-gray eyes. His brown vest and green shorts are made of wool felt and he wears a white short-sleeved shirt with turned-up sleeves. The heavy wool knit socks, which vary in color, and handmade black leather shoes with brown laces, give him a hiker's appearance. He has a brown plaid cotton knapsack, with a twine drawstring, held in place on his back with leather straps.

Illustration 55. Peter with his curly blonde hair.

Illustration 56. Another example of Peter with his knapsack.

Elizabeth

Elizabeth (1981 to 1984), seen in Illustrations 57, 58 and 59, from the Little Children Series I, is a limited edition of 250 and 17 inches tall. She has very pretty blue-gray eyes and her very dark hair is brushed to the side and held in place by a maroon felt bow. Her dusty rose-colored cotton dress has a white apron over it. Her shoes vary. Elizabeth is often referred to as the mate or companion to William (see Illustrations 60 and 61).

Illustration 57. Elizabeth with her dark hair brushed to the side.

Illustration 58. Another version of Elizabeth carrying a book.

Illustration 59. A third version of Elizabeth, also carrying a book.

William

William (1981 to 1984), seen in Illustrations 60 and 61, from the Little Children Series I, is a limited edition of 250. He has black curly hair and brown eyes and wears a blue corduroy two-piece romper trimmed with white buttons and a white collar. His white felt tie shoes are unique. He is possibly the only R. John Wright doll with this type of shoe. He makes a good companion for Elizabeth (see Illustrations 57, 58 and 59).

Illustration 60. William with his curly black hair.

Illustration 61. Another view of William.

Jesse

Jesse (1982), seen in Illustrations 62 and 63, from the Little Children Series I, is a limited edition of 250. A handsome boy with brown hair and eyes, he has a little cap set loosely on his head. He wears a brown bomber-style jacket over a cotton shirt in a fine brown plaid and knickers that come in a variety of colors. His hands are usually stuck in his pockets, which looks really cute. His shoes are brown leather and his socks are brown cotton.

Illustration 62. Jesse wearing burgundy corduroy knickers.

Illustration 63. Jesse in green corduroy knickers.

Lillian (1981 to 1984), seen in Illustrations 64 and 65, is a limited edition of 250 dolls made in 1983. She has brown eyes and short red hair covered by a cap of heavy rust-colored yarn stitched together in an unusual pattern and trimmed with a green yarn bow. She wears a rust plaid jumper over a white blouse, brown cotton socks and handmade brown leather shoes.

Illustration 64. Lillian, a limited edition of 250.

Illustration 65. Another Lillian with a slightly different expression on her face.

Illustration 66. Tad
with his fishing pole.

Tad (1981 to 1984), seen in Illustration 66, from the Little Children Series I, is a limited edition of 250 and the most unusual of the children. With a brown mohair wig and brown eyes, he is 17 inches tall with a very sweet look about him. His hair is cut to expose his ears so that the detail of the ears can be seen. He is dressed in very plain colors, a striped long-sleeved shirt, white cotton pants, brown handmade leather oxfords and carries a fishing pole with a string and cork on the end.

Edward and His Rum-a-Tum Drum

Illustration 67. Edward and His Rum-a-Tum Drum, an exclusive for The Enchanted Doll House.

Edward and His Rum-a-Tum Drum (1985), seen in Illustration 67, is a limited edition of 150 made exclusively for The Enchanted Doll House. He has a blonde mohair wig and brown eyes. His cap matches his wine-colored velveteen two-piece outfit with a ruffled collar and cuffs and he wears white cotton socks and black leather shoes. His drum is trimmed out in wood and has a leather strap attached that goes over his shoulders. He holds a drumstick in each hand.

Scott and Lisa (1985 to 1986), seen in Illustrations 68 through 72, are from the Little Children Series II. Although they were sold in separate boxes, they were dressed alike and each is a limited edition of 250.

Illustration 68. Scott and Lisa, sold separately but dressed alike.

Illustration 69. Another set of Scott and Lisa.

Scott

Scott has blue eyes and short blonde hair with a curl to it. He wears gray shorts with a white shirt, a red knit vest and brown oxfords. Over his shoulder, he has a brown leather school bag with pencils and a book. Variations can be found in the shades of the oxfords as well as the school bag. The socks vary from brown tweed to off-white and some examples do not have the knit hat. The colors of the hats and sweaters can also vary.

Illustration 70. Scott with a brown leather school bag.

Illustration 71. Scott with a dark brown leather school bag and wearing a knit hat and "bow" tie.

Lisa

Lisa has blonde mohair parted down the middle with two braids and very unusual light brown eyes. She wears a red knit sweater to match Scott's vest, a white blouse, a gray pleated skirt and white socks with her brown leather shoes. She carries her white cat.

Illustration 72. Lisa holding her white cat.

Childhood Classics

Captain Corey

Captain Corey (1982), seen in Illustration 73, is a limited edition of 50, made especially for The Enchanted Doll House, then owned by Jean Schramm. He has red hair and brown eyes and wears a blue two-piece suit consisting of a lightweight blue twill jacket and short pants. His shirt has a white collar and cuffs and a big red plaid bow at the neck. His shoes are black leather with white cotton socks. In his hand is a wonderful wooden boat painted red, green and off-white with black trim. Across his hat is gold lettering reading "S. S. ENCHANTED."

Illustration 73. Captain Corey and his boat.

Timothy and Rosemary

Timothy and Rosemary (1983), seen in Illustrations 74A and 74B, are a limited edition of 50 pairs from the Babes in Toyland Series I. Timothy has short curly light brown hair, wears gray pajamas trimmed in white with rose-colored buttons and carries his jointed teddy bear and plaid blanket. Rosemary has a light brown mohair wig with tiny braids, wears a gray nightgown trimmed in white with white buttons and carries a doll.

Illustration 74A. Timothy from the Babes in Toyland Series I.

Illustration 74B. Rosemary from the Babes in Toyland Series I.

The Little Prince Premiere Edition (1983 to 1984), seen in Illustration 75, is a limited edition of 250 sold exclusively by The Toy Shoppe of Midlothian, Virginia, and was based on the drawings in the book *The Little Prince,* written and illustrated by Antoine de Saint-Exupery. He has short blonde tousled hair, deep brown eyes and on his chest, he wears a silver medallion. He wears a full-length green cloak lined in rust felt over his white one-piece jump suit. The jumpsuit has a gold felt cummerbund that snaps in the back at the waist. There are matching gold cuffs and gold stars on his shoulders. His knee-high felt boots are gray and in his hand, he holds a wonderful stainless steel sword about eight inches long.

Illustration 75. The Toy Shoppe's exclusive Little Prince. Since this one is a prototype, it is not numbered. The box has been marked "prototype" and is signed by R. John Wright.

Emily and The Enchanted Doll

Emily and The Enchanted Doll (1984), seen in Illustration 76, is a limited edition of 150 dolls, an exclusive for The Enchanted Doll House. Emily has beautiful gray eyes and a blonde mohair wig pulled to the back, with short bangs and a big white cotton bow in the back of her head. She wears a white cotton batiste lace-trimmed dress, white cotton socks and black felt shoes. In her arms, Emily carries her doll, wearing a pink polished cotton dress with lace-trimmed pantaloons and hat to resemble the logo of The Enchanted Doll House.

Illustration 76. Emily and The Enchanted Doll, an exclusive for The Enchanted Doll House.

Max and His Pinocchio

Max and His Pinocchio (1985), seen in Illustration 77, a limited edition of 150, was made exclusively for Geppetto's Toys in New York. Max has very dark brown hair and very pale gray-green eyes. He wears a typical lederhosen outfit in gray felt trimmed in black with a white shirt, a dark green felt hat with gold cord around the crown and off-white socks with brown felt strap shoes. In his arms, he carries Pinocchio who is painted with red clothing and a pointed hat. Pinocchio has the name "Geppetto's Toys" stamped in gold across his chest.

Illustration 77. Max and His Pinocchio, an exclusive for Geppetto's Toys in New York.

Michael and Lindsay

Michael and Lindsay (1984 to 1985), seen in Illustrations 78 and 79, are a limited edition of 250 pairs from the Babes in Toyland Series II. Michael has a blonde mohair wig and wears olive-green felt pajamas. He is carrying his brown velveteen rabbit and a plaid blanket. Lindsay has light green eyes and blonde hair which is done up in braids over her head. Her olive-green nightgown is trimmed with lace at the collar and her brown slippers are trimmed with blue pompons. She carries a sleeping baby in a christening dress and bonnet in her arms.

Illustration 78. Michael with his rabbit and blanket.

Illustration 79. Lindsay with her sleeping baby.

Illustration 80. Rachel - Sunday Best, an exclusive for Hobby Center Toys, Bea Skydell's and The Village Toy Shoppe.

Rachel - Sunday Best (1985 to 1986), seen in Illustration 80, a limited edition of 250 dolls, was sold exclusively through Hobby Center Toys, Bea Skydell's and The Village Toy Shoppe. She has very dark brown hair and either very light gray-green or brown eyes. The only variation with this doll, other than her eyes, is in the facial colors with some being more vivid than others. She wears a blue velvet dress with a square neckline trimmed in lace, brown cotton socks and black leather shoes. In her arms, she carries her own doll, which has long blonde hair and wears a gray dress with a tiny cherry print. The dolls' slip and underwear are trimmed with lace and she wears red high-top boots.

Arthur and Lillian (1987 to 1989), seen in Illustrations 81, 83 and 84, are a little brother and sister limited edition set of 500 that won the DOTY award in February of 1987. Two of the Wright's children — Arthur, age five, and Lillian, age seven, accepted the DOTY award for their father dressed as models of the dolls (see Illustration 82).

Arthur is 18 inches tall with blonde hair and is dressed in a sailor suit and hat. The sailboat he carries has white sails and is painted orange on the bottom. Lillian is 20 inches tall with red hair and wears a blue sailor dress with white socks and Mary Jane shoes. She carries a jump rope. About 100 sets came boxed as a pair while the others were boxed individually.

Illustration 81. Arthur and Lillian, DOTY award winners in 1987.

Illustration 82. The Wright children, Arthur and Lillian, accepting the DOTY award, and are dressed to represent the dolls.

Illustration 83. Arthur with his sailboat.

Illustration 84. Lillian with her jump rope.

Patrick and His Bear (1987 to 1988), seen in Illustration 85, is a limited edition of 250 and is named after one of the Wright children. He has brown eyes and red tousled hair. Patrick wears overalls, which are just like the major brand overalls, except that the overall buttons have "RJW" embossed on them. There are deep pockets on the side for tools as well as a hanky pocket in the back. His shirt is red and blue plaid with buttons down the front. He wears heavy gray socks with red trim and brown leather shoes. Patrick carries a light brown fully-jointed mohair bear.

Illustration 85. Patrick and His Bear.

The Enchanted Doll

The Enchanted Doll (1989), seen in Illustration 86, was made in a limited edition of 500 exclusively for Jean Schramm of the logo doll for The Enchanted Doll House. The first 250 were signed by R. John Wright and shipped in 1989 with the remainder shipped in 1990. Standing 14 inches tall, she has black hair and brown eyes and wears the traditional pink and white checked dress with matching bonnet, white apron and high button leather boots. She carries her matching umbrella.

Illustration 86. The Enchanted Doll, the logo doll for The Enchanted Doll House.

Little Red Riding Hood

Little Red Riding Hood (1988 to 1991), seen in Illustration 87, was a limited edition of 500. A wolf was shown in one of the ads with Little Red Riding Hood but only one prototype was ever made and the wolf was never produced. Little Red Riding Hood wears a white blouse and apron over a gray skirt with a red cape and black leather shoes. She carries a handmade basket of some unique items: a loaf of bread made at a local baker and then covered with several coats of shellac, a box of tea, a wedge of cheese and a pear, all of which were made especially for this doll. The cutest part of the whole piece is the box of tea in the basket. It says "T E A Original felt dolls//R. John Wright" and the back of the box reads "This is a meticulous blend of the finest teas from Cambridge, New York. R. John Wright Tea is a favorite tea of grandmothers, who appreciate its warm aroma, bold, bright flavor and curative powers. Guaranteed to soothe the stomach after over-eating. R. John Wright tea//Exclusive importer, Cambridge, N. Y."

Illustration 87. Little Red Riding Hood with her basket of goodies.

Hans Brinker

Hans and Gretel Brinker (1990 to 1992), seen in Illustrations 88 and 89, a limited edition of 350 pairs, are based on the book *Hans Brinker or the Silver Skates*, by Mary Mapes Dodge, a story of the life in Holland, published by Grosset & Dunlap.

Hans is 20 inches tall and is the first R. John Wright doll constructed with jointed knees, enabling him to sit or stand in a skating position. He has blonde hair and pale blue eyes. He wears blue-green knickers with brown and turquoise knee patches sewn on, a tan jacket with checked collar and cuffs, a blue-green felt cap and a knit wine-colored scarf. His very unique skates are slung over his shoulder.

Illustration 88. Hans Brinker with his skates.

Gretel Brinker

Gretel Brinker is 18 inches tall and has the regular jointed body. Her hair is brown and she has light blue eyes. She wears a brown felt jumper with an off-white blouse, an apron and a blue felt jacket with a plaid scarf around her neck. Her cap is in the typical Dutch style and she wears white woolen socks and wooden shoes. In her arms, she carries a bundle of twigs.

Illustration 89. Gretel Brinker carrying a bundle of twigs.

The Little Prince Centary Edition

The Little Prince Centary Edition (2000), seen in Illustration 90, is a limited edition of 1000 based on the original book and illustrations by the author. Celebrating the 100th anniversary of author Antoine de Saint-Exupery's birth, the Little Prince is 15 inches tall, fully-jointed and made of the finest all-wool felt. Each doll is individually numbered and comes with a signed and numbered certificate, as well as a card for the owner's registration.

Illustration 90. The Little Prince Centary Edition. *Photo courtesy of R. John Wright Product Catalog.*

Heidi and Her Goat, Snowflake

Heidi (2000), and Her Goat, Snowflake , seen in Illustration 91, a limited edition of 500 sets with each doll numbered and accompanied by a signed certificate of authenticity, is sold exclusively by Little Switzerland Dolls in Hampton, New York. Standing 17-1/2 inches tall, Heidi is constructed of the highest quality all-wool felt with delicately hand-painted features. She is fully-jointed, her limbs are molded with sculptural detail and her hands are expressive with each finger molded separately. Felt flowers encircle her dark mohair wig. In her arms, she carries Snowflake, a wonderful newborn baby goat with felt horns, hooves and glass eyes. Plus he wears a little bell attached to his leather collar. His nose and mouth are delicately embroidered. His neck is jointed and his body is made of a wire armature.

Illustration 91. Heidi and her goat, Snowflake. *Photo courtesy of R. John Wright Product Catalog.*

Nursery Rhyme Series

In 1993, R. John Wright introduced the Nursery Rhyme Series as limited editions of 100. These were made for special doll shops and were sold exclusively through them. Dolls like these earned R. John Wright the coveted Jumeau trophy in 1994 — one of the most prestigious awards that can be given to a doll artist.

Mary, Mary, Quite Contrary

Mary, Mary, Quite Contrary (1992), seen in Illustration 92, a limited edition of 100, was sold through Dolly Dears in Birmingham, Alabama, from 1992 to 1993 and was the first of this series issued. Her brown hair is pulled back into two braids and she stands 17 inches tall. She wears a white cotton dress with applied green felt dots under an apricot-colored cotton work apron with six pockets which ties in the back. She also wears a broad-brimmed tan wool felt hat with a black velvet ribbon around the crown. Her shoes are black felt slip-ons over white cotton socks. She carries a wooden rake with the handle painted like wood and the rake painted silver to look like metal.

Illustration 92. Mary, Mary, Quite Contrary with her rake.

Jack

Jack and Jill (1993), seen in Illustrations 93 and 94, a limited edition of 100 pairs, were boxed together and sold as a set exclusively through The Toy Shoppe in Midlothian, Virginia.

Jack has short tousled auburn hair and brown eyes. He is wearing black wool knickers and a white shirt with ruffles at the neck and sleeves. He has black and orange striped wool knit socks with black cloth high-top shoes. Over this, he wears a mauve smocked cotton coat with four large black buttons. On his head is a pointed rust wool felt hat.

Illustration 93. Jack with his pointed hat.

Jill

Jill has brown eyes and a dark brown mohair wig styled with green felt bows on either side of her face. She wears a soft yellow cotton dress with applied white dots and smocking on the bodice. She has green and gray striped socks with black high-top boots. She carries the ultimate accessory — the wonderful wooden bucket that looks old.

Illustration 94. Jill carrying her wooden bucket.

Little Boy Blue

Little Boy Blue (1993), seen in Illustration 95, a limited edition of 100, was sold through Dolly Dears in Birmingham, Alabama. Inspired by the art of the famous illustrator, Jessie Wilcox Smith (1863 to 1935), he stands 17 inches tall and has brown hair and blue eyes. He wears blue shorts with a blue and white striped shirt covered with a blue smock. He has a tan hat and wears striped socks with his black felt slip-on shoes. A Swiss horn with a rope attached at its side is hung loosely around his neck.

Illustration 95. Little Boy Blue and his Swiss horn.

Little Miss Muffet

Little Miss Muffet (1993), seen in Illustration 96, a limited edition of 100, was made exclusively for Dee's Doll and Bear Cottage in Salt Lake City, Utah. She has blonde hair and blue eyes and wears a dusty rose-colored dress with white dots under a long white apron that ties in the back. Her white bonnet is trimmed to match her dress. She carries a wooden bowl filled with curds and whey and carries a metal spoon (which may discolor and leave a mark on the doll's hand).

Illustration 96. Little Miss Muffet with her bowl and spoon.

Tom, the Piper's Son, scheduled to be the final piece in the Nursery Rhyme Series, was advertised in July 1993 as being produced for a doll shop in Indiana. To date, it has not been produced.

Winnie-the-Pooh Series

While under license of the Walt Disney Company, R. John Wright came up with a beautiful collection of characters of which Christopher Robin and Winnie-the-Pooh were the first.

In 1925, A. A. Milne started writing about his five-year-old son, Christopher, playing in his mother's garden with his teddy bear. In the garden was an old hollow tree with a big hole in it, and that is how the story was started. Two books were published, *Winnie-the-Pooh* in 1926 and *The House On Pooh Corner* in 1928. Walt Disney purchased the rights to Winnie-the-Pooh from A. A. Milne in the 1950s and started developing the Winnie-the-Pooh series in the 1960s.

In 1985, Christopher Robin and Winnie-the-Pooh Series I were introduced at the International Toy Fair in New York City. These dolls, based on the illustrations of E. H. Shepard and produced under license from the Walt Disney Company, created quite a sensation and were featured on the NBC "Today" show as the winner of the first Doll of The Year (DOTY) Award. The production of this series brought R. John Wright world-wide recognition. The production of Winnie-the-Pooh was the beginning of the bear-making part of John's career.

Christopher Robin and Winnie-the-Pooh Series I

Christopher Robin and Winnie-the-Pooh Series I (1985 to 1986), seen in Illustration 97 (Christopher Robin can also be seen in Illustration 100), is a limited edition of 1000. Christopher Robin is 18 inches tall with light brown hair and eyes. He wears a blue cotton jacket and brown pants with an off-white hat and brown leather shoes. Winnie-the-Pooh is 8 inches tall and fully-jointed. He wears a red jersey knit short jacket.

Illustration 97. Christopher Robin and Winnie-the-Pooh Series I.

Winnie-the-Pooh

Winnie-the-Pooh (1985 to 1986), seen in Illustration 98, is a limited edition of 2500 and stands 8 inches tall. Fully-jointed, he is light brown and wears an off-red jersey jacket. He came in a see-through cover box. One of the set in the animal series of Winnie-the-Pooh, this is the same bear that came with the Christopher Robin and Winnie-the-Pooh Series I set.

Illustration 98. Winnie-the-Pooh, standing 8 inches tall.

Christopher Robin Series II

Christopher Robin Series II (1986 to 1987), seen in Illustrations 99 and 100, is a limited edition of 500. He has light brown hair and eyes and wears shorts, held up by suspenders, and a white knit shirt. Over this, he wears his yellow raincoat and hat with matching umbrella with a wooden handle. Some raincoats have been found with loops and a belt while later ones have none. The raincoat has slash type pockets on the outside of the coat and two big square pockets inside. He wears knee-high black rubber boots.

Illustration 99. Christopher Robin Series II with his umbrella.

Illustration 100. Christopher Robin from Series I and Christopher Robin Series II with his umbrella.

Piglet

Piglet (1986 to 1987), seen in Illustration 101, is a limited edition of 1000 and stands 5 inches tall. Fully-jointed, Piglet is made of wool felt and wears a green knit suit that is stitched down the back. He comes in a see-through cover box.

Illustration 101. Piglet in his green romper.

Eyore

Eeyore (1986 to 1987), seen in Illustration 102, is a limited edition of 1000 and is 6 inches long. His neck and legs are jointed and he has black shoe-button type eyes. He comes in a see-through cover box.

Illustration 102. Eeyore with jointed neck and legs.

Kanga and Roo

Kanga and Roo (1987 to 1988), seen in Illustration 103, is a limited edition set of 1000. Kanga is 9-1/2 inches tall, jointed at the neck and lower legs only with eyes just like Tigger's and a nice white pouch that Roo fits snugly into. Roo is not jointed and has tiny black beady eyes. Made of dark brown wool with white fronts, they come in a see-through cover box.

Illustration 103. Kanga and Roo.

Tigger

Tigger (1987 to 1988), seen in Illustration 104, is a limited edition of 1000 and is 6 inches long. Made of wool felt, he is fully jointed, with white shoe-button type glass eyes with black dots and sits nicely in his see-through cover box.

Illustration 104. Tigger with his shoe-button type eyes.

Lifesize Pooh

Lifesize Pooh (1987 to 1988), seen in Illustration 105, is a limited edition of 2500 and the largest bear to date. Fully-jointed, he is 18 inches tall, made of wonderful mohair plush and wears his traditional little red sweater buttoned at the neck. He came boxed.

Illustration 105. Lifesize Pooh, the largest bear to date.

Lifesize Piglet

Lifesize Piglet (1987 to 1988), seen in Illustration 106, is a limited edition of 1000 and stands 9 inches tall. Fully-jointed, he is made of wool felt with a removable green knit suit. He came in a cardboard box.

Illustration 106. Lifesize Piglet in his green knit suit.

Piglet with Violets

Piglet with Violets (1988 to 1989), seen in Illustration 107, is a limited edition of 2500 and stands 7 inches tall. Fully-jointed, he is made of wool felt and wears the green knit suit. He is holding a handful of purple violets.

Illustration 107. Piglet with Violets.

Illustration 108. Winnie-the-Pooh and His Favorite Chair.

Winnie-the-Pooh and His Favorite Chair

Winnie-the-Pooh and His Favorite Chair (1989), seen in Illustration 108, is a limited edition of 500 and produced exclusively for the Second Annual Walt Disney World™ Teddy Bear and Doll Convention in Orlando Florida, sponsored by Walt Disney World™. Pooh is 10 inches tall, fully-jointed and made of English mohair/wool plush with glass eyes The chair, 10 inches tall, is made of 100 percent wool felt and was produced according to R. John Wright's design by the Hallagan Manufacturing Company, a well known manufacturer of regular size furniture. The set is packaged in a unique box that looks like a house. It opens at the top to reveal the wonderful set inside it.

Winnie-the-Pooh with the Honey Pot (1987 to 1989), seen in Illustrations 109, 110 and 111, is a limited edition of 5000 and 14 inches tall. Fully-jointed, with a bee resting on his right ear, he came in two shades of mohair plush — the traditional light brown mohair and a darker brown mohair with a matted look. Pooh is holding a lidded honey pot that has "HUNNY" written on tape and attached to the side of the pot. His bib can be found inside.

Illustration 109. Both versions of Winnie-the-Pooh with the Honey Pot.

Illustration 110. Winnie-the-Pooh with the Honey Pot, made of the traditional light brown mohair.

Illustration 111. Winnie-the-Pooh with the Honey Pot, made of the darker brown mohair with a matted look. He is wearing his bib.

Wintertime Pooh and Piglet (1995), seen in Illustration 112 with Wintertime Christopher Robin, is a limited edition set of 250 sold exclusively for FAO Schwarz. Pooh is 5 inches tall, fully-jointed and made of mohair plush. Piglet is 2-1/2 inches tall, jointed at the neck and arms and made of felt. They are each wearing their winter scarves.

Illustration 112. Wintertime Christopher Robin with his sled and Wintertime Pooh and Piglet.

Wintertime Christopher Robin (1999), seen in Illustration 112 with Wintertime Pooh and Piglet, is out of chronological order so he can be shown with Wintertime Pooh and Piglet. Wintertime Christopher Robin is a very limited special edition of 250 sold primarily through FAO Schwarz. Standing 12 inches tall, Christopher Robin has a wool felt sculpted body, a knotted mohair wig, a hand-painted face and is fully jointed at the neck, shoulders and hips. He is wearing a felt-lined corduroy overcoat and hat with rubber boots. His accessory is a replica of an antique wooden sled of wood with metal runners.

Wintertime Eeyore

Wintertime Eeyore (1996), seen in Illustration 113, is a limited edition of 250, sold exclusively by FAO Schwarz. Fully jointed and made of mohair plush, Eeyore is 3-1/2 inches tall and comes with a wooden house made of sticks held together with wire hinges and a piece of rope wound up in one corner. Eeyore has a patch of snow over his back and on his neck. There is a cute little storybook in the box, telling how Pooh worried about Eeyore not having a place to live while it was snowing, so he and his friend, Piglet, made the house for Eeyore. Little extras like these make R. John Wright characters so special.

Illustration 113. Wintertime Eeyore and his house of sticks.

Holiday Winnie-the-Pooh

Holiday Winnie-the-Pooh (1997), seen in Illustration 114, is a limited edition of 1000, which nearly sold out at the Tenth Annual Walt Disney World™ Doll and Teddy Bear Convention in 1997. Standing 12 inches tall and fully-jointed, he is made of mohair plush and has a scarf wrapped around his neck and torso. His little mouth is open and a bit of his tongue is showing. He holds a piece of handmade felt holly in his paw and is wearing big high-top rubber boots.

Illustration 114. Holiday Winnie-the-Pooh with his sprig of holly.

Jingle Bell Pooh (1998), not shown, is a limited edition of 35 which were made exclusively for the employees of R. John Wright Dolls. Standing 12 inches tall and fully-jointed, this mohair plush bear has a felt bow and a brass bell.

King Christopher Robin

King Christopher Robin (1998), seen in Illustration 115, is a very limited edition of 30 made for EXPO WEST held June 12 to 14, 1998. King Christopher Robin is based on the original E. H. Shepard illustration which accompanied a poem "If I Were King" in the classic *Winnie the Pooh* books by A. A. Milne. Including his crown, he measures 14 inches tall. This outfit is exactly like that in the illustration with a white shirt, blue shorts, belt, socks and sandals. He wears a burgundy Jacquard cape and sports a play sword in a leather scabbard that hangs loosely down the front. He has an army of assorted miniature soldiers, all custom-made and hand-painted. Each set is numbered and has a signed and numbered certificate.

Illustration 115. King Christopher Robin followed by his army.

Classic Winnie-the-Pooh

Classic Winnie-the-Pooh (1998 to 1999), seen in Illustration 116, is a limited edition of 2500 and comes in a heavy blue wool felt drawstring bag. Standing 12 inches tall, he is made of mohair plush and is fully-jointed. He has an embroidered nose and tiny black shoe-button type eyes.

Illustration 116. Classic Winnie-the-Pooh with his blue wool felt drawstring bag.

Nighttime Winnie-the-Pooh

Nighttime Winnie-the-Pooh (1998 to 1999), seen in Illustration 117, is a limited edition of 2500. Standing 12 inches tall and fully-jointed, he is made of the finest mohair plush and is wearing a cotton nightshirt and cap, blue felt slippers and carries a tin candlestick. He came in a display box with a certificate and registration of ownership papers. He is often shown with the Bear Bed (1999), a limited edition of 500. This painted iron bed is 8 inches wide by 15 inches long by 12 inches high. It has an assortment of bedding pieces with it.

Illustration 117. Nighttime Winnie-the-Pooh shown with the Bear Bed.

Illustration 118. The painted iron Bear Bed and bedding.

Pocket Pooh

Pocket Pooh (1993), seen in Illustration 119, is a limited edition of 3500. He is shown out of chronological order, so that he can be seen with the other pocket animals. The first of the pocket animals, he is fully-jointed, 5-1/2 inches tall and wears a little red jacket. Most of the Pocket Poohs were the traditional gold color, but along the way, there was a change of color to more of a brown.

Illustration 119. Two Pocket Poohs.

Pocket Piglet

Pocket Piglet (1994), seen in Illustration 120, is a limited edition 3500 and stands 3 inches tall. He is also shown out of chronological order so that he can be seen with the later pocket animals. His torso is his blue felt suit with three buttons and he is jointed at the arms.

Illustration 120. Pocket Piglet.

Pocket Eyore

Pocket Eeyore (1995), seen in Illustration 121, is a limited edition of 3500 and is 3-1/2 inches tall. Fully-jointed, he is made of mohair plush.

Illustration 121. Pocket Eeyore.

Pocket Tigger

Pocket Tigger (1996), seen in Illustration 122, is a limited edition of 3500 and stands 3-1/2 inches tall. Fully-jointed, he is made of mohair plush.

Illustration 122. Pocket Tigger.

Santa Pooh (1993), not shown, is a very limited edition of 25. Standing 5 inches tall and fully-jointed, he is made of mohair plush and wears a plush and felt Santa hat with a brass button on it. This edition was part of the regular Pocket Pooh edition.

Pocket Rabbit

Pocket Rabbit (1998 to 1999), seen in Illustration 123, is a limited edition of 3500 and stands 5-1/2 inches tall. Fully-jointed, he is made of mohair plush.

Illustration 123. Pocket Rabbit.

Pocket Series, Christopher Robin

From the Pocket Series, Christopher Robin (1997 to 1999), seen in Illustration 124, is a limited edition of 3500. He is 12 inches tall, jointed at the neck, made of felt and anatomically correct.

Illustration 124. Christopher Robin.

Pocket Owl

Pocket Owl (1999), seen in Illustration 125, is a limited edition of 3500 and stands 4 inches tall. He is jointed at the neck with movable wings, glass eyes and all-wool beak and feet. The wonderful coloring on his plush mohair was achieved through airbrushing.

Illustration 125. Pocket Owl.

Pocket Kanga and Roo

Pocket Kanga and Roo (1999), seen in Illustration 126, is a limited edition of 3500. Kanga is 5-1/2 inches tall with jointed legs and neck and is made of mohair plush. Roo is 1-1/2 inches tall and made of felt with a jointed head.

Illustration 126. Pocket Kanga and Roo.

A lithograph backdrop for the pocket series (1998 to 1999) 19 inches by 24 inches, not shown, was produced in an unnumbered limited edition of 1000. The full-color lithograph is mounted on a folding board.

Christopher Robin and Pocket Pooh

Christopher Robin and Pocket Pooh (1998 to 1999), seen in Illustration 127, is a limited edition set of 1500. Christopher Robin is 12 inches tall and jointed at the neck while Winnie-the-Pooh is a 5-1/2-inch fully-jointed bear.

Illustration 127. Christopher Robin and Pocket Pooh are shown with the Pocket series: Pocket Tigger, Pocket Piglet, Pocket Rabbit, Pocket Eeyore, Pocket Owl and Pocket Kanga and Roo.

Partytime Pocket Eeyore and Tigger

Partytime Pocket Eeyore and Tigger (1996), seen in Illustration 128, is a special limited edition set of 100 made to commemorate the 25th anniversary of Walt Disney World™ in 1996. Eeyore has a pink cotton bow on his tail and Tigger has a party hat on his head.

Illustration 128. Partytime Pocket Eeyore and Tigger.

The production and shipment of all of the pocket series characters and other Walt Disney Company items concluded on December 31, 1999.

PoohBee

PoohBee (1999), seen in Illustration 129, is a limited edition of 500, made exclusively for Teddys in Hamilton Square, New Jersey. Standing 8-inches tall and fully-jointed, he is made of mohair plush and wears a bee costume of yellow and black woven mohair fabric and a felt cap with antennae. He comes complete with a stinger and is holding a sprig of felt clover in his paw.

Illustration 129. PoohBee in his bee costume.

Christopher Robin and Pooh Bedtime

Christopher Robin and Pooh Bedtime (1999), seen in Illustration 130, is a limited edition set of 500 with the first 250 offered to collectors at the 12th Annual Walt Disney World™ Teddy Bear and Doll Convention in 1999. These came with a nightcap on Pooh's head. The remaining 250 are offered through authorized retail dealers and do not have the nightcap. Based on the works of A. A. Milne and E. H. Shepard, Christopher Robin stands 17-1/2 inches tall, has brown hair and eyes, is fully-jointed and made entirely of felt. He is wearing his print pajamas over which he wears his a wool felt burgundy robe with handmade leather slippers. Pooh, who accompanies him, is 7-1/2 inches tall and made of mohair.

Illustration 130. Christopher Robin and Pooh Bedtime.

Snow White Series

While John was under contract to the Walt Disney Company, he set his sights on creating the Snow White and Seven Dwarfs characters. He worked on this project over two years before he was satisfied with his work. In the meantime, he visited the Walt Disney Company studio archives in California, aided by Martha Armstrong-Hand, whose husband was the supervising director of the original film. John's Snow White and the Seven Dwarfs were shown at Toy Fair in 1988. The edition was supposed to have been 2500, but production was from 1989 to 1993 and only 1500 sets were produced. Of those advertised, only 1000 sets were made and sold as matched numbers. There were two Snow White dolls produced, one as Snow White Princess, the other as Snow White in Rags. Snow White and the Dwarfs were all based on the Walt Disney Company film.

It was at this time, with Snow White, that the Wrights began an innovative process of molding not only the faces but the feet and hands. This was taken a step further with Geppetto who also has separate fingers.

Snow White Princess and Snow White Rags

Illustration 131. Snow White Princess and Snow White in Rags together.

Snow White in Rags

Snow White in Rags (1989 to 1993), seen in Illustrations 131, 132 and 134, is a limited edition of 1000. Standing 15 inches tall, her costume is based on that seen in the film. She wears wooden shoes and carries a wooden bucket.

Illustration 132. Snow White in Rags with her bucket.

Snow White Princess

Snow White Princess (1989 to 1994), seen in Illustrations 131, 133 and 135, is based on the Walt Disney Company film and created in the Disney colors. The dark-haired princess has a maroon felt bow in her hair and wears a pale yellow felt skirt, a dark blue bodice with lighter blue short sleeves with brown bands and a white cotton cowl-type collar under a brown felt cape lined with deep red felt. Her gray felt heels each have a white felt bow on them.

Illustration 133. Snow White Princess.

Snow White in Rags and the Seven Dwarfs

Illustration 134. Snow White in Rags and the Seven Dwarfs, made from 1989 to 1994.

Snow White Princess and the Seven Dwarfs

Illustration 135. Snow White Princess and the Seven Dwarfs, made from 1989 to 1994.

Illustration 136. Doc.

Illustration 137. Bashful.

Illustration 138. Dopey.

Illustration 139. Frightened Dopey (1992) a limited edition of 250, 9 inches tall with a pouty look.

Illustration 140. Frightened Dopey and Dopey together.

Illustration 141. Sleepy.

Illustration 142. Sneezy.

Illustration 143. Happy.

Illustration 144. Grumpy.

Pinocchio Series

R. John Wright's next creations stemmed from the story and the Walt Disney Company movie Pinocchio.

Pinocchio

Pinocchio (1992), seen in Illustration 145, a limited edition of 500, was designed by R. John Wright and sculpted in wax, then sent to the famous wood-carvers, ANRI, in Italy. There the wooden parts were produced to his specifications. However, Pinocchio was assembled, dressed and wigged at the R. John Wright factory. The 9-inch Pinocchio was constructed entirely of alpine maple with hand-carved detail and is fully jointed. He is hand-painted with a dark hand-knotted mohair wig and wears an all wool felt costume dyed to match the authentic colors in the Walt Disney Company film, including his hat with the little red feather.

Illustration 145. Pinocchio, sculpted in wax and produced in alpine maple by the ANRI Company.

Pleasure Island Pinocchio

Pleasure Island Pinocchio (1992), seen in Illustration 146, a limited edition of 250, was made exclusively for the Walt Disney Company. This was the same size as the Pinocchio seen in Illustration 145 and is dressed the same as the earlier Pinocchio with two exceptions — this version has a long gray felt tail and a pair of donkey ears.

Illustration 146. Pleasure Island Pinocchio with his donkey ears and tail.

Geppetto and Pinocchio II
Traditional

Geppetto and Pinocchio II Traditional (1994 to 1995), seen in Illustration 147, is a limited edition of 250. Geppetto, who is 17 inches tall, is made entirely of felt and was created with a ball and socket jointed knee, enabling him to sit. Pinocchio is the traditional 10-inch wooden jointed boy. The chair Geppetto is sitting on was carved by John to be identical to the chair in the Walt Disney Company film. It was then sent to ANRI in Italy to be produced in an edition of 500.

Illustration 147. Geppetto and Pinocchio Traditional Series II.

Illustration 148. Geppetto's chair, reproduced by ANRI and based on the one in the movie.

102

Geppetto and Pinocchio I Marionette

Geppetto and Pinocchio I Marionette (1994 to 1995), seen in Illustration 149, is a limited edition of 500. This is the same as Geppetto and Pinocchio Traditional Series II except that Pinocchio is a marionette.

Illustration 149. Geppetto and Pinocchio Marionette Series I.

Geppetto Searches for Pinocchio

Geppetto Searches for Pinocchio (1996), seen in Illustration 150, was produced as a limited edition of 250. He is made of molded felt and is fully jointed. Geppetto carries his lantern and wears a brown coat, a red hat and a blue wool scarf.

Illustration 150. Geppetto Searches for Pinocchio.

Beatrix Potter™ Series

In 1998, R. John Wright introduced Peter Rabbit™—the first in an exciting series based on the characters of Beatrix Potter. The fully-jointed Peter Rabbit™, a soft and most realistic looking rabbit, was soon followed by Jemima Puddle-duck™ and Benjamin Bunny™, each meticulously detailed and crafted out of mohair.

Peter Rabbit™

Illustration 151. Two Peter Rabbits™. The one on the right has the whiskers.

Peter Rabbit™ (1998), seen in Illustrations 151 and 152, a limited edition of 2500, is 12 inches tall. Made of custom woven mohair plush with embroidered features and glass eyes, Peter Rabbit™ wears his classic blue coat with brass buttons and leather slippers. He comes with and without his whiskers and is holding a handcrafted felt English radish.

Jemima Puddle-duck™ and Peter Rabbit™

Illustration 152. Jemima Puddle-duck™ joins Peter Rabbit™.

Jemima Puddle-duck™

Jemima Puddle-duck™ (2000), seen in Illustrations 152, 153 and 154, a limited edition of 1500, is the second in the Beatrix Potter™ Series. She is 15 inches tall, made of white alpaca plush with a felt beak, webbed feet and glass eyes, and is wearing a paisley-patterned shawl and a blue poke bonnet.

Illustration 153. Jemima Puddle-duck™ in her signature bonnet and shawl.

Jemima's Ducklings™ (2000), seen in Illustrations 154 and 155, a limited edition of 1000 sets of four, come boxed together as a set with a fifth egg that never hatched. Jemima's Ducklings™ are each 3-1/2 inches tall and made of mohair with jointed necks, glass eyes, felt beaks and feet.

Illustration 154. Jemima's Ducklings™ shown with Jemima Puddle-duck™.

Illustration 155. Close-up of Jemima's Ducklings™ and the unhatched egg.

Benjamin Bunny™

Benjamin Bunny™ (2000), seen in Illustration 156, a limited edition of 1500, is 12 inches tall. Made of mohair plush, Benjamin Bunny™ is fully-jointed with glass eyes, air-brushed coloring and embroidered detailing. He wears his tam-o'-shanter and brown wool jacket with his wood and leather clogs. He carries a handcrafted felt and organdy onion.

Illustration 156. Benjamin Bunny™ with his onion. *Photo courtesy of R. John Wright Product Catalog.*

Illustration 157. The Garden Wheelbarrow filled with vegetables. *Photo courtesy of R. John Wright Product Catalog.*

The Garden Wheelbarrow

The Garden Wheelbarrow (2000), seen in Illustration 157, is a limited edition of 500. This detailed piece is handcrafted of weathered yellow pine, an authentic replica of an antique English wheelbarrow. It measures approximately 12 inches long and 6 inches high, and is filled with handmade wool felt fresh lettuces and vegetables.

Kewpie® Editions

In 1999, the R. John Wright Kewpie® was introduced. The first Kewpies® were created by Rose O'Neill in 1909 and have been produced in a variety of media. This is the first time Kewpies® have been made of molded felt.

"Fleur" Flower Kewpie®

"Fleur" Flower Kewpie® (1999), seen in Illustrations 158 and 160, is a limited edition of 250. Made exclusively for the United Federation of Doll Clubs' National Convention in 1999, she is 6 inches tall, fully jointed and entirely made of felt. She has a flower hat and a dress of petals. Only those who attended the R. John Wright dinner were given the opportunity to purchase "Fleur" Flower Kewpie®.

Illustration 158. "Fleur" Flower Kewpie® in her petal dress and flower hat.

"Flit" Kewpie® Bug

"Flit" Kewpie® Bug (1999), seen in Illustrations 159 and 160, is a limited edition of 250. A companion to "Fleur" Flower Kewpie®, "Flit" Kewpie® Bug is 6 inches tall and fully-jointed with a flower in his hands. Only those who attended the R. John Wright dinner were given the opportunity to order "Flit" Kewpie® Bug.

Illustration 159. "Flit" Kewpie® Bug with the flower in his hand.

Illustration 160. "Flit" Kewpie® Bug and "Fleur" Flower Kewpie®.

Boutonniere Kewpie®

Boutonniere Kewpie® (2000), seen in Illustration 161, is a limited edition of 2500 and 2 inches tall. Designed to be used as a pin, it is made of all wool felt with hand-painted features.

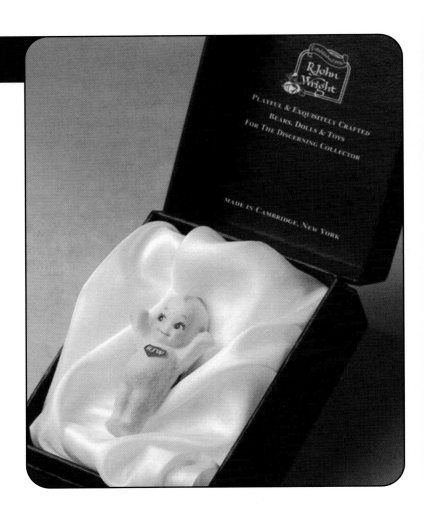

Illustration 161. Boutonniere Kewpie®, designed to be worn as a pin. *Photo courtesy of RJW Collector.*

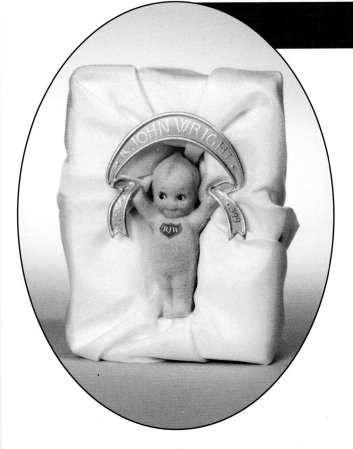

UFDC Boutonniere Kewpie®

Illustration 162. UFDC Boutonniere Kewpie®, the souvenir from the R. John Wright dinner at the UFDC National Convention in 1999. This is from a special limited edition of 250 made as the table souvenirs for the United Federation of Doll Clubs' (UFDC) R. John Wright dinner at the 1999 National Convention which both the artist and his wife attended. The UFDC Boutonniere Kewpie® holds a light blue banner, which has been added, with "UFDC R. JOHN WRIGHT 1999" embossed in gold on it.

Klassic Kewpie®

Klassic Kewpie® (2000), seen in Illustration 163, is a limited edition of 1000, inspired by the early bisque Kewpies® made in Germany in the early 1900s. Made of 100 percent wool felt and delicately hand-painted, Klassic Kewpie® is 8 inches tall with jointed arms, legs and neck. He has a fine wisp of mohair on his forehead to add to his charm.

Illustration 163. Klassic Kewpie®, inspired by the original bisque Kewpies®.

Hottentot Kewpie®

Hottentot Kewpie® (2000), seen in Illustration 164, a limited edition of 1000, was inspired by the early bisque Kewpies® originally designed by Rose O'Neill and made in Germany about 1912. Made of the finest chocolate brown all-wool felt, Hottentot Kewpie® is 6 inches tall and has the trademark shield on his chest.

Illustration 164. Hottentot Kewpie®. *Photo courtesy of RJW Collector.*

Millennium Kewpie®

Millennium Kewpie® (2000), seen in Illustration 165, a limited edition of 1000, is 6 inches tall. Fully-jointed and made of wool felt, Millennium Kewpie® wears a tiny molded felt top hat, carries an "ebonized" wooden walking stick embellished with a gold leaf and has a satin sash commemorating the new Millennium.

Illustration 165. Millennium Kewpie® with its satin sash and walking stick. *Photo courtesy of R. John Wright Product Catalog.*

Baby Bear Collection

In 1998, John and Susan Wright traveled to Singapore and made a very special store appearance at Precious Things owned by Anna Kahlenburg. The article about his trip is in volume three, number four of the *RJW Collector,* the collectors' club newsletter. This store carries R. John Wright's first Panda, Bao-Bao, which was released in September 2000. This is the first edition of the Baby Bear Collection, consisting of five distinctive realistic bear cubs in custom mohair plush. Each baby bear comes with his own signed and numbered certificate as well as forms for the owner's registration.

Bao-Bao

Bao-Bao (2000), seen in Illustration 166, is a limited edition of 500, sold exclusively by Precious Things in Singapore. Fully-jointed and 12 inches tall, the panda cub is made of the finest mohair plush, with a felt nose, an open mouth with a felt tongue, imported glass eyes and pawpads with resin claws. In one paw, he holds a stalk of bamboo, also crafted of wool felt. Bao-Bao means "baby" in Chinese.

Illustration 166. Bao-Bao, R. John Wright's first Panda cub, is also the first edition in the Bear Collection.

Joey (2000), not shown, a limited edition of 500 and is sold directly through R. John Wright Dolls, Inc., only. Made of mohair, he has glass eyes, pawpads, resin claws, a molded felt nose and embroidered details. In one paw, he holds a sprig of eucalyptus fashioned out of felt. Joey, the first Koala created by R. John Wright, is the fifth and final edition in the Baby Bear Collection. Part of the proceeds from the sale of Joey will go toward Koala conservation efforts.

Tickles

Tickles (2000), seen in Illustration 167, is a limited edition of 500, sold exclusively through The Toy Shoppe in Richmond, Virginia. Fully-jointed with bent baby legs and 12 inches tall, he is made of the finest brown mohair plush with beautiful airbrushed shading, a leather nose, felt pawpads, molded claws and glass eyes. In one paw, he holds a branch of blueberries handcrafted from felt. Tickles is the second edition in the Baby Bear Collection.

Illustration 167. Tickles, a brown bear cub, the second edition in the Baby Bear Collection. *Photo courtesy of RJW Collector.*

Nippy

Nippy (2000), seen in Illustration 168, is a limited edition of 500, sold exclusively through Campbell's Collectibles of Crown Point, Indiana. Made of the finest white mohair plush, he is 12 inches tall with felt pawpads, an open mouth with a felt tongue, a molded felt nose, molded claws and glass eyes. He holds a fish made of felt with glass eyes and airbrushed detail. Nippy, the first polar bear made by R. John Wright, is the third edition in the Baby Bear Collection and comes packaged in his own presentation box.

Illustration 168. Nippy, a white polar bear cub, is the third edition in the Baby Bear Collection. *Photo courtesy of RJW Collector.*

Pep

Pep (2000), seen in Illustration 169, is a limited edition of 500, sold exclusively by Village Bears and Collectibles in Sarasota, Florida. Made of the finest mohair plush, he is 12 inches tall with felt paws, a molded leather nose, molded claws and glass eyes. In one paw, he holds a branch of acorns and oak leaves handcrafted of felt. Pep, a black bear cub, comes in a custom-made box and is the fourth edition in the Baby Bear Collection.

Illustration 169. Pep, a black bear cub, is the fourth edition in the Baby Bear Collection.

One-of-a-Kind Editions

R. John Wright has created four one-of-a-kind pieces and each one has been better then the last. All of them have been auctioned off at the Annual Walt Disney World™ Teddy Bear and Doll Convention or the Walt Disney World™ Disneyana Convention in Orlando, Florida, and have sold for phenomenal prices.

The Mining Cart (1989), not shown, was made in 1989 for the 3rd Annual Walt Disney World™ Teddy Bear and Doll Convention held in 1989 at Disney World™ in Orlando, Florida. The Mining Cart is the first of R. John Wright's one-of-a-kind pieces to be made for this venue. John designed the fully-jointed dwarf, Sleepy, with his mining pick, sitting in a handcrafted wooden cart filled with diamond ore and pulled by a molded wool felt one-of-a-kind reindeer in its complete harness. This piece is owned by Danny Shapiro and is on display at The Toy Shoppe in Richmond, Virginia.

Winnie-the-Pooh's Christmas Holiday (1997), not shown, is the second one-of-a-kind made for the celebration of the 10th Annual Walt Disney World™ Teddy Bear and Doll Convention in 1997. This piece features Christopher Robin, dressed in his fur-trimmed hooded snowsuit with mittens, boots and handcrafted lantern, caroling with Winnie-the-Pooh in his boots and felt scarf. The other characters — Eeyore, Piglet, Kanga and Roo, Owl and Rabbit — are also in their finery as depicted in the original artwork. It is set in a display 22 inches high, 24 inches wide and 28 inches long. The figures are all done in wool felt and mohair fur, against a hand-painted watercolor background of an outdoor scene. This creation sold for $27,000.

This Calls For a Celebration (1998), not shown, is the third one-of-a-kind made for the Seventh Annual Walt Disney World™ Disneyana Convention, held in Orlando, Florida, in September 1998. This three-dimensional scenic tableau is based on the scene in the movie when Pinocchio turns into a real live boy. This exclusive set includes Geppetto, with his working concertina, dancing with Pinocchio who has been brought to life by the Blue Fairy. Pinocchio has always been made of wood but in this setting, he was produced of felt. The display box is 22 inches high, 24 inches wide and 28 inches long. The figures are all posed against a hand-painted background of Geppetto's workshop, based on the original film. This piece sold for $18,000.

Vespers (1999), seen in Illustration 170, is the fourth one-of-kind made for the 12th Annual Walt Disney World™ Teddy Bear and Doll Convention in 1999. Opened, the three-dimensional scene is 20 inches high, 28 inches wide and 26 inches deep and is based upon Christopher Robin's Nursery as depicted by E. H. Shepard in the *Winnie-the-Pooh* books by A. A. Milne. It is custom-made and hand-decorated for the period. The furniture included is a youth bed, coat rack, clothing and accessories.

Christopher Robin is on his knees and Pooh is in his nightcap. Also included are Piglet, Eeyore, Kanga and Roo and Tigger. Stevenson Bros. in England made the hand-carved rocking horse. They are all posed in front of a window showing the Hundred Acre Wood at dusk. This one-of-a-kind piece went for a record price of $36,000.

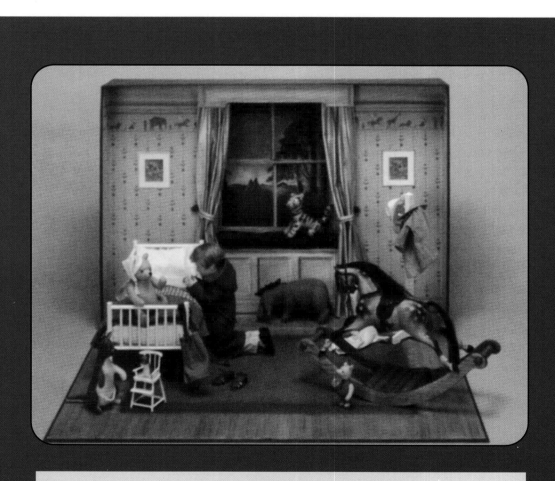

Illustration 170. Vespers, R. John Wright's fourth one-of-a-kind, made for the 12th Annual Walt Disney World™ Teddy Bear and Doll Convention in 1999.

Current Editions

Curious George Series
Curious George (2000), not shown, is a limited edition of 1500, based on the famous character created by Margaret and H. A. Rey. Standing 9-inches tall, the monkey is constructed of custom-made Alpaca plush with a molded felt face, glass eyes and is fully jointed. He has felt hands and feet with individual fingers and toes and comes with his yellow hat made of wool felt. Curious George comes in his own presentation box with a signed certificate of authenticity and owner's registration papers.

Paddington™ Collection

Paddington™ Bear (2000), seen in Illustration 171, a limited edition of 2500, is based on the famous character created by Michael Bond. Standing 15 inches tall and fully jointed, Paddington Bear is constructed of custom-woven Alpaca plush with glass eyes, a leather nose, hand-embroidered features and felt pawpads. His trademark duffel coat is green with red lining and the dark green bush hat is made of all-wool felt. He carries a custom-made leather suitcase, handcrafted to a perfect scale. Each piece comes in its own presentation box, with a signed certificate of authenticity and owner's registration papers. Future plans include additional accessories and clothing made especially for Paddington™.

Illustration 171. Paddington™ Bear in his duffel coat and green hat. *Photo courtesy of RJW Collector.*

Collector Club Series

In 1996, the R. John Wright Company started the exclusive RJW Collectors' Club. Members receive a quarterly full-color publication — *The RJW Collector* — produced with photographs and information on R. John Wright creations, past, present and future. There are also interesting topics on related subjects such as Emma Adams's Columbian Rag doll article and an article on doll storage and preservation.

In addition to the newsletter, other services are available exclusively to members of the club. These services include the RJW Marketplace; the RJW Calendar; the RJW Hotline; and the opportunity to purchase the Club Edition for that year. The RJW Marketplace is a free classified ad service. The RJW Calendar contains information on signings and official release dates for upcoming RJW editions. Finally, the RJW Hotline is a toll-free telephone service for members.

Finally, members of the R. John Wright Collectors' Club have the priviledge to purchase Club Exclusive dolls.

Golliwog

The Premiere Club Exclusive was Golliwog, seen in Illustrations 172 and 174, and was produced from 1996 to 1998 in an edition of 1526. He is 11 inches tall, fully-jointed and made from black wool felt.

Illustration 172. Golliwog, the Premiere Club Exclusive.

Two Club Exclusives are scheduled for 2000/2001 club year. Gollibabies celebrate the RJW Collector's Club fifth anniversary. Another offered to Charter Members is the RJW Bear Boutonniere.

For further information on the R. John Wright Collectors' Club, contact the club at 15 West Main Street, Cambridge, New York 12816; telephone: 1-888-258-2759; fax: 518-677-5202; e-mail: rjwclub@aol.com or visit the website at http://www.rjohnwright.com.

Miss Golli

Miss Golli, seen in Illustrations 173 and 174, was produced from 1997 to 1998 in an edition of 849. She is 11 inches tall, fully-jointed and made of molded felt. She wears a darling dress to match Golliwog.

Illustration 173. Miss Golli, the second club exclusive.

Illustration 174.
Miss Golli and Golliwog.

Teddy Bear

Teddy Bear, seen in Illustration 175, was produced from 1997 to 1998 in an edition of 866. He is a 9-inch brown mohair plush bear that is fully jointed. The look on his face makes him especially cute.

Illustration 175. Teddy Bear.

Silly Old Bear

Silly Old Bear, seen in Illustration 176, was produced from 1998 to 1999 in an edition of 720. He is a 7-inch sitting off-white mohair bear with jointed arms and neck. His neck is weighted with pellets and he comes in a wool drawstring bag.

Illustration 176. Silly Old Bear in his drawstring bag.

Periwinkle

Periwinkle, seen in Illustration 177, was produced from 1998 to 1999 in an edition of 807. He is 6 inches tall, seated on a deep red pincushion and is made of molded felt, with jointed arms and neck. The trademarked logo for the R. John Wright Company, this one is almost identical to the earlier Periwinkle.

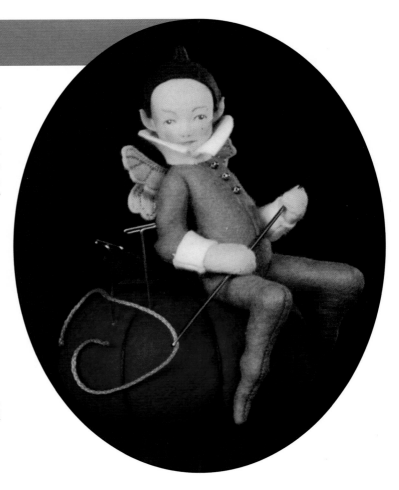

Illustration 177. Periwinkle, the R. John Wright Company's trademarked logo as a club exclusive.

Kewpie® and Teddy

Kewpie® and Teddy, produced from 1999 to 2000, seen in Illustration 178, is a wonderful club edition inspired by the art of Rose O'Neill. Kewpie® is 6 inches tall with hand-painted features on the finest of all-wool felt. His buddy is a 3-1/2-inch tall miniature mohair teddy bear with hand-embroidered features that is fully jointed.

Illustration 178. Kewpie® and Teddy.

$\mathcal{P}$rice Guide

NAME	YEAR OF ISSUE	EDITION SIZE	RETAIL PRICE	CURRENT VALUE
A1 (see Mario)				
Arthur (see also Arthur and Lillian)	1987 - 1989	250	$575	$800 - $1000
Arthur and Lillian	1987 - 1989	500 boxed sets	$1,100 set	$1800, pair
B2 (see Old Lady With Rake)				
Backdrop/Winnie-the-Pooh	1998 - 1999	1000	$185	$185
Bao-Bao	2000	500	$595	$595
Bashful	1989 - 1994	2500	$325	$350 - $400
Bear Boutonniere (see RJW Bear Boutonniere)				
Bear's Bed	1999	500	$350	$350 - $375
Becky	1981 - 1984	250	$330	$1150 - $1250
Benjamin Bunny™	2000	1500	$625	$625
Bernard	1979 - 1981	NA	$255	$1350 - $1450
Boutonniere Kewpie®	2000	2500	$185	$185
Boutonniere Kewpie® (see UFDC Boutonniere Kewpie®)				
Bridget	1979 - 1981	NA	$100	$1350 - $1450
Captain Corey	1982	50	$380	$3800 - $4000
Christina	1977 - 1978	NA	$60	$1200 - $1250
Christopher Robin (pocket series)	1997 - 1999	3500	$895	$895
Christopher Robin (see King Christopher Robin)	1998	30	$1695	$1950 - 2000
Christopher Robin (see Wintertime Christopher Robin)				
Christopher Robin II	1986 - 1987	500	$575	$2200 - $2500
Christopher Robin and Pooh	1997 - 1999	1500 sets	$1,325	$1325
Christopher Robin and Winnie-the-Pooh Series I	1985 - 1986	1000	$595	$2500 - $2750
Christopher Robin and Pooh Bedtime	1999	500 sets	$1,850	$1850
Classic Winnie-the-Pooh	1998 - 1999	2500	$475	$475
Curious George	2000	1000	$565	$565
Doc	1989 - 1994	2500	$325	$350 - $400
Dopey	1989 - 1994	2500	$325	$350 - $400
Dopey (see Frightened Dopey)				
Ducklings (see Jemima's Ducklings™)				
Edward and His Drum	1985	150		$1350 - $1450
Eeyore	1986 - 1987	1000	$95	$375 - $450

NAME	YEAR OF ISSUE	EDITION SIZE	RETAIL PRICE	CURRENT VALUE
Eeyore (see Partytime Tigger and Eeyore)				
Eeyore (see Pocket Eeyore)				
Eeyore (see Wintertime Eeyore)				
Elizabeth	1981 - 1984	250	$275	$1150 - $1200
Elsa	1979 - 1981	NA	$100	$1250 - $1350
Emily and the Enchanted Doll	1984	150		$1500 - $1650
Emma	1979 - 1981	NA	$100	$1250 - $1350
Enchanted Doll, the	1989	500	$515	$750 - $850
Enchanted Doll, the (see Emily and the Enchanted Doll)				
Erica	1979 - 1981	NA	$235	$1250 - $1350
F1 (see Giuseppi)				
Father Christmas	1977 - 1978	NA	$100	$1100 - $1200
"Fleur" Flower Kewpie® — with "Flit" Kewpie® Bug, matching numbers	1999	250	$595	$2100, pair
"Flit" Kewpie® Bug — with "Fleur" Flower Kewpie®, matching numbers	1999	250	$595	$2100, pair
Frightened Dopey	1992	250	$575	$575
G2	1977 - 1978	NA	NA	$1200 - $1250
Garden Wheelbarrow	2000	500	$395	$395
George (see Curious George)				
Geppetto (see This Calls For A Celebration)				
Geppetto and Pinocchio Marionette Series I	1994 - 1995	500	$2350	$2350
Geppetto and Pinocchio II Traditional	1994	250	$2150	$1,875
Geppetto Searches for Pinocchio	1996	250	$1875	$1,250
Geppetto's Chair	1992	500		$500 - $550
Giuseppi	1977 - 1978	NA	$70	$1600 - $1750
Golli (see Miss Golli)				
GolliBabies	2001	(club)	$675, pair $350, each	
Golliwog	1996 - 1997	1526 (club)	$535	$650 - $750
Gretchen	1979 - 1981	NA	$225	$1350 - $1450
Gretel Brinker (see Hans and Gretel Brinker)				
Grumpy	1989 - 1994	2500	$325	$350 - $400
Guido	1979 - 1981	NA	$100-$245	$1250 - $1350
H2 (see Maria)				
Hannah	1981 - 1984	250	$275	$1150 - $1250
Hans and Gretel Brinker	1990 - 1992	350 pairs	$1500, pair	$2150 - $2250, pair
Happy	1989 - 1994	2500	$325	$350 - $400
Heidi and her goat, Snowflake	2000	500 sets	$1,650	$1650

NAME	YEAR OF ISSUE	EDITION SIZE	RETAIL PRICE	CURRENT VALUE
Holiday Winnie-the-Pooh (Disney)	1997	1000		$600 - $700
Hottentot Kewpie®	2000	1000	$425	$425
J1 (never produced)	1977 - 1978	NA	NA	NA
Jack and Jill	1993	100 pairs	$1695, pair	$1900 - $2100, pair
Jemima Puddle-duck™	2000	1500	$655	$655
Jemima's Ducklings™	2000	1000 sets	$975	$975
Jenny	1979 - 1981	NA	$100	$1200 - $1250
Jesse	1981 - 1984	250	$325	$1150 - $1250
Jill (see Jack and Jill)				
Jingle Bell Pooh	1998	35	NA	NA
Joey	2000	500	$595	
K2 (see Christina)				
Kanga (see Pocket Kanga and Roo)				
Kanga and Roo	1987 - 1988	1000	$95	$375 - $450
Karl	1979 - 1981	NA	$225	$1250 - $1350
Kate	1979 - 1981	NA	$225	$1250 - $1350
Kewpie® (see Boutonniere Kewpie®)				
Kewpie® (see Classic Kewpie®)				
Kewpie® (see "Fleur" Flower Kewpie®)				
Kewpie® (see "Flit" Kewpie® Bug)				
Kewpie® (see Hottentot Kewpie®)				
Kewpie® (see Millennium Kewpie®)				
Kewpie® (see UFDC Boutonniere Kewpie®)				
Kewpie® and Teddy	2000	(club)	$525	$535
King Christopher Robin	1998	30	$1695	$1950 - $2000
Klassic Kewpie®	2000		$475	$475
L1 (see Old Man With Stick)				
Lifesize Piglet	1987 - 1988	1000	$95	$400 - $450
Lifesize Pooh	1987 - 1988	2500	$165	$1500 - $1750
Lillian	1981 - 1984	250	$555	$1150 - $1200
Lina	1979 - 1981	NA	$255	$1250 - $1350
Lindsay (see Michael and Lindsay)				
Lisa	1985 - 1986	250	$525	$1000 - $1100
Lithographed Backdrop	1998 - 1999	100	$185	$185
Little Boy Blue	1993	100	$850	$1200 - $1250
Little Miss Muffet	1993	100	$855	$1100 - $1150
Little Prince Centary Edition, The	2000	1000	$1,275	$1275
Little Prince Premiere Edition, The	1983 - 1984	250	$425	$3800 - $4000
Little Red Riding Hood	1989 - 1991	500	$875	$1150 - $1250
Luigi	1977 - 1978	NA	$70	$1350 - $1400
M1 (see Rosa)				

NAME	YEAR OF ISSUE	EDITION SIZE	RETAIL PRICE	CURRENT VALUE
MacTavish	1979 - 1981	NA	$100	$1250 - $1350
Maria	1977 - 1978	NA	$60	$1200 - $1250
Mario	1977 - 1978	NA	$60	$1250 - $1350
Marion	1979 - 1981	NA	$100	$1350 - $1450
Mary, Mary Quite Contrary	1992	100	$850	$1100 - $1200
Max and Pinocchio	1985	150	$485	$2250 - $2500
Michael and Lindsay	1984 - 1985	250 pairs		$950, each
Millennium Kewpie®	2000	1000	$485	$485
Mining Cart With Deer	1989	One-of-a-kind	NA	NA
Miss Golli	1997 - 1998	849 (club)	$535	$650 - $750
Nighttime Winnie-the-Pooh	1998 - 1999	2500	$595	$595
Nippy	2000	500	$595	$595
Old Lady With Chicken	1977 - 1978	3	NA	$1250 - $1500
Old Lady With Rake	1977 - 1978	NA	$60	$1200 - $1250
Old Man	1976	NA	NA	$1200 - $1250
Old Man With Stick	1977 - 1978	NA	$60	$1200 - $1300
Old Woman	1976	NA	NA	$1200 - $1250
Owl (see Pocket Owl)				
P1 (see Luigi)				
Paddington™ Bear	2000	2500	$650	$650
Paddy (with clay pipe)	1979 - 1981	NA	$225	$1450 - $1500
Partytime Tigger and Eeyore (Disney)	1999	100		$625 - $675, pair
Patrick and His Bear	1987 - 1988	250	$575	$1000 - $1150
Pep	2000	500	$595	$565
Periwinkle	1978-1979	NA	$45	$1250 - $1500
Periwinkle (pincushion)	1999	807 (club)	$385	$400 - $425
Peter	1981 - 1984	250	$330	$1350 - $1450
Peter Rabbit™	1998 - 1999	2500	$595	$595
Piglet (5 1/2")	1986 - 1987	1000	$48	$375 - $450
Piglet (see Lifesize Piglet)				
Piglet (see Pocket Piglet)				
Piglet with Violets	1988 - 1989	2500	$145	$450 - $500
Pinocchio	1992	500	$625	$850 - $950
Pinocchio (see Geppetto and Pinocchio I Marionette)				
Pinocchio (see Geppetto and Pinocchio II Traditional)				
Pinocchio (see Geppetto Searches for Pinocchio)				
Pinocchio (see Max and Pinocchio)				
Pinocchio (see Pleasure Island Pinocchio)				
Pinocchio (see This Calls For A Celebration)				

NAME	YEAR OF ISSUE	EDITION SIZE	RETAIL PRICE	CURRENT VALUE
Pinocchio - Disney Edition (16")	2000	500	$1500	$1500
Pleasure Island Pinocchio	1992	250		$1500 - $1750
Pocket Christopher Robin	1998 - 1999	3500	$895	$895
Pocket Eeyore	1995	3500	$295	$295
Pocket Kanga and Roo	1999	3500	$345	$345
Pocket Owl	1999	3500	$310	$310
Pocket Piglet	1994	3500	$225	$350 - $400
Pocket Pooh	1993	3500	$285	$450 - $500
Pocket Rabbit	1998	3500	$295	$295
Pocket Tigger	1996	3500	$295	$295
Pooh (8" only)	1985 - 1986	2500	$95	$750 - $850
Pooh (see Christopher Robin and Pooh Bedtime)				
Pooh (see Christopher Robin and Pooh)				
Pooh (see Classic Winnie-the-Pooh)				
Pooh (see Holiday Winnie-the-Pooh)				
Pooh (see Jingle Bell Pooh)				
Pooh (see Lifesize Pooh)				
Pooh (see Nighttime Winnie-the-Pooh)				
Pooh (see Pocket Pooh)				
Pooh (see Santa Pooh)				
Pooh (see Winnie-the-Pooh's Christmas Holiday)				
Pooh (see Wintertime Pooh and Piglet)				
PoohBee	1999	500	$450	$750 - $850
Rabbit (see Pocket Rabbit)				
Rachel - Sunday Best	1985 - 1986	250	$450	$1350 - $1450
RJW Bear Boutonniere	2000	(club)	$185	In Production
Roo (see Kanga and Roo)				
Roo (see Pocket Kanga and Roo)				
Rosa	1977 - 1978	NA	$60	$1850 - $2000
Rosemary (see Timothy and Rosemary)				
S1 (see Father Christmas)				
Santa Pooh	1993	25	NA	NA
Scott	1985 - 1986	250	$525	$1000 - $1100
Seth	1979 - 1981	NA	$100	$1650 - $1750
Seven Dwarfs (see Snow White and the Seven Dwarfs Sets)				
Silly Old Bear	1999	720 (club)	$325	$325 - $350
Sleepy	1989 - 1994	2500	$325	$350 - $400
Sneezy	1989 - 1994	2500	$325	$350 - $400

NAME	YEAR OF ISSUE	EDITION SIZE	RETAIL PRICE	CURRENT VALUE
Snow White and nine-piece set, matched numbers	1989 - 1994	1000	$2790	$4800 - $5000
Snow White and the Seven Dwarfs Sets	1989 - 1994	1500 sets (less actually made)	$2,790	$3500 - $3750
Snow White In Rags	1989 - 1993	1000	$600	$750 - $850
Snow White Princess	1989 - 1984	2500	$580	$750 - $850
St. Nicholas	1979 - 1981	250	$230	$1150 - $1250
Tad	1981 - 1984	250	$275	$1150 - $1200
Teddy (see Kewpie® and Teddy)				
Teddy Bear	1997 - 1998	866 (club)	$375	$375 - $400
This Calls For A Celebration	1998	One-of-a-kind	$18,000	NA
Tickles	2000	500	$595	$595
Tigger	1987 - 1988	1000	$95	$375 - $450
Tigger (see Partytime Tigger and Eeyore)				
Tigger (see Pocket Tigger)				
Timothy and Rosemary	1983	50 pairs.	NA	$3800 - $4000, each
UFDC Boutonniere Kewpie®	1999	250	Table Souvenier	$225 - $250
Vespers	1999	One-of-a-kind	$36,000	NA
William	1981 - 1984	250	$230	$1200 - $1250
Winnie-the-Pooh (see Christopher Robin and Winnie-the-Pooh)				
Winnie-the-Pooh (see Classic Winnie-the-Pooh)				
Winnie-the-Pooh (see Holiday Winnie-the-Pooh)				
Winnie-the-Pooh (see Nighttime Winnie-the-Pooh)				
Winnie-the-Pooh and His Favorite Chair	1989	500	$750	$2250 - $2500
Winnie-the-Pooh's Christmas Holiday	1997	One-of-a-kind	$27,000	NA
Winnie-the-Pooh with Honey Pot	1987 - 1989	5000	$220	$850 - $950
Wintertime Pooh and Piglet	1995	250 set		$750 - $850, pair
Wintertime Christopher Robin	1998 - 1999	250	$1,250	$1250
Wintertime Eeyore	1995	250	$543.75	$725

Index

About the Author

The author, Shirley Bertrand, was born in Menomonie, Wisconsin. Raised on a dairy farm, she has a great love for all animals. Her education began in a one-room school, Hudson Road School, which she attended through eighth grade. She completed her high school education at Menomonie Public High School.

Shirley moved to Chicago, Illinois, in 1955, to seek her "fortune." She was soon married and became the mother of four children — two boys and two girls.

In 1965, she started repairing and dressing dolls in her home. Gradually she worked towards opening Shirley's Dollhouse in Wheeling, Illinois. Shirley's Dollhouse recently celebrated its 25th anniversary in business.

Shirley's collecting did not stop at dolls. She has a collection of collections. Antique dolls have always been her love, from the beginning. However, in the late 1980s, she bought her first R. John Wright doll and this was the beginning of her collection of and passion for his works. This is now one of her favorite collections.

In order to write this book, it was important to have photographs of as many R. John Wright dolls and characters as possible. This was quite easy for Shirley as she owns an example of nearly every piece made by R. John Wright. We are grateful that she has chosen to share them with us.

Shirley, a member of the Lake County Doll Club and the United Federation of Doll Clubs, Inc., lives on a farm with her collections of dogs, cats and horses. Nowadays, her favorite pastime is sharing her time with her grandchildren.